Milieu Therapy
in
Schizophrenia

Also by Dr. Artiss (as Editor)
THE SYMPTOM AS COMMUNICATION
IN SCHIZOPHRENIA

Milieu Therapy
in
Schizophrenia

By

LIEUTENANT COLONEL KENNETH L. ARTISS, MC

Foreword by

DEXTER M. BULLARD, M.D.

Introduction by

DAVID McK. RIOCH, M.D.

GRUNE & STRATTON · 1962
NEW YORK · LONDON

Library of Congress Catalog Card Number 61-17274

Printed and bound in U.S.A. (B)

CONTENTS

FOREWORD

THIS SLIM VOLUME contains a fascinating account of an experiment in therapy conducted by the Ward Officer, who is a career Army psychiatrist, a registered nurse, also a career Army officer, enlisted men of the Army (medical technicians) ranging in rank from private to sergeant, and lastly by patients themselves. It is, or perhaps used to be, a frequently heard comment among civilian psychiatrists that the military organization—the relationship between officers and enlisted men— precluded the establishment of the necessary trust for psychotherapy to be effective. Such views must be thoroughly revised in the light of the data presented in this work.

The majority of psychiatrists with whom I have had experience regard themselves as the most important members of the therapeutic team (in hospital practice), yet comparatively few recognize the importance they should give to the training and use of others as therapeutic agents. The author's emphasis on the part played by nurses and technicians in their contacts with patients, both individually and in group therapy sessions, is warranted and is in contrast to the weight given to the fewer individual psychotherapeutic interviews held between patient and doctor. This structuring reminds one of the way Harry Stack Sullivan, in his Sheppard and Enoch Pratt Hospital days, used to work through his attendants on the special ward set up for the treatment of young schizophrenics. Sullivan, however, never published in any detail his methods of working through others so we are greatly indebted to Colonel Artiss for his extensive and detailed accounts of this undertaking.

Exhortations about the value of training nurses and aides and then using them in the treatment program are so commonplace they may be almost dismissed as cliches, yet the difficulties of welding the members of a group into a team with a common philosophy of psychopathology from which stems a common philosophy of treatment are portrayed so vividly and in such detail that the magnitude of the task is often quite discouraging to the psychiatrist who would do more than render lip service to the cliche.

The work required is enormous but equally enormously rewarding when the areas of trust and distrust, expectancy, tension levels and the effects of repetitive annoyances can be mutually explored by patients and staff and the resultant increased understanding brought to bear on the psychopathology shared by patients and staff. Over the past ten years in our own work at Chestnut Lodge, we have become increasingly aware of the deleterious effect on patients of feelings and attitudes on the part of our therapists, nurses and aides, whose blindness to this aspect of themselves has reduced the effectiveness of their work. More and more it is becoming apparent that there is psychopathology exhibited by members of the alleged therapeutic community, as well as by the patient community.

Among the purposes of this research project, two call for special mention; first, the therapeutic goal itself, i.e., the return to military duty of schizophrenic patients within an arbitrarily set time limit of six months. The high percentage of returns to duty reported here indicated the essential correctness of the assumptions made about the problems of milieu therapy and the steps taken to solve them.

The second purpose of the project has been to see if what has been learned by Colonel Artiss and his staff can be taught to other psychiatrists and, in turn, to other groups of technicians in other Army hospitals.

The initial data seem to indicate that a competent psychiatrist can learn to be a leader of a group, a catalytic agent—though not without change in himself—and a teacher of his staff, and that the therapeutic results obtained are not dependent on the personality and high competence of the author. Six other psychiatrists have been able to further the work with comparable effectiveness.

It has been a pleasure for the writer to serve as a consultant to three of the successive psychiatrists in charge of this research, to share in the discussion of the many problems presented for the first time to both the Army psychiatrists and civilian consultant and to hear that out of our discussions has come occasionally something useful to the members of the therapeutic team.

It is my hope that the Army will continue to support this work, for out of it has and will continue to come, in addition to therapeutic results, new and different concepts of hospital management—i.e., milieu therapy—which will have utility ranging greatly beyond one ward in one hospital. If other hospitals, both public and private, would undertake similar investigative efforts based on the essential philosophy of this work, in a few years time data should become available which would indicate whether or not milieu therapy, as conceived here, could become a substantial, if not a major, part of hospital practice. The implications of this work actually call into question some concepts of therapy which place almost exclusive emphasis on individual psychotherapy. In any event, such questions can only be successfully explored with further data made available by similar research in other hospitals.

Dexter M. Bullard, M.D.
Chestnut Lodge
Rockville, Maryland

INTRODUCTION

SOCIAL PSYCHIATRY has developed increasingly rapidly during the past 20 years, more as an extension and maturation of several lines of work and thought in the general field of psychiatry than as a separate sub-specialty. Much of its recent growth has occurred as a part of the general improvement of psychiatric services, through the efforts of many workers using the trial-and-error method to improve the care of patients and to prevent chronic hospitalization. A considerable variety of more formal clinical investigations of the therapeutic utilization of social factors have also been independently initiated and conducted by physicians in different settings. Based on the recognition of the considerable role social factors play in determining the onset, symptomatology and course of the mental syndromes, these investigations have been directed toward identifying the significant factors and developing techniques for manipulating them for the benefit of the patients and their community. These clinical studies have ranged from investigating the utilization of medical, occupational and social facilities in the community to working out the problems of creating a therapeutic community in the hospital. Not least in importance have been the studies of combining hospital and community resources as responsibility, such as by the "open ward" or "open hospital" systems, by providing day-hospitals and by instituting "clubs" with resident nurse or counsellor where former patients can stay for limited periods.

Concomitantly with the recent interest in administrative and social psychiatry, there has been a remarkable change in the attitude of both professional and non-professional members of hospital staffs to the patients. Whereas, earlier, patients were chiefly regarded as "cases," as "schizophrenics," "manics," "paranoids," and so on, they are now looked on much more as "persons" who are ill or who have certain symptoms. The patient as a "person" is seen as having a social role, with the expectation of appropriate communication and responsibility in the role, including the expectation of a significant degree of recovery. The contrast with the inevitable herding of hopeless "cases" in the "back wards"— with public and professional agreement that these "cases" no longer belonged in society—is quite phenomenal. Indeed, one hesitates to try to retrieve the sense and, as it were, the flavor of one's own attitude toward this problem as it was as little as 25 years ago. Although the possibility of psychotherapy[a] and the effectiveness of the structured ward community[b] had been demonstrated previously and so-called spontaneous recoveries were well known, it would appear that the convulsive and psychopharmacological therapies have played a major role in facilitating this widespread change in attitude toward mental patients. The unrealistic optimism, which was earlier frequently expressed, suggesting that these therapies would rapidly provide a "cure" for "mental disease" has not been fulfilled. It has been, however, replaced by a more useful attitude directing attention to careful study of the biological course of the mental syndromes and the effective use of the organic therapies for controlling *particular symptoms*. The assurance that in a high proportion of instances socially disruptive symptoms—such as "panic" states, aggressive-assaultive and self-destructive behavior, and so on—can be controlled without loss of social communication, represents one of the major contributions of the present era to hospital psychiatry. Much of the improvement in the social relations of patients appears to stem from this accomplishment. These considerations raise a further question, namely, whether the over-all therapeutic effect of organic therapies may not be exercised chiefly through the re-establishment of social communication. Whatever the answer to this and to other related questions may prove to be, it is now generally recognized that the external social milieu in which any specific-therapeutic operation (including psychotherapy) is conducted is as important for the psychiatrist as the internal milieu is for the internist or the surgeon.

Most of the recent clinical developments in social psychiatry have been based on empirical observations. However, the theoretical basis for social psychiatry was well advanced considerably before the recent growth of clinical interest in this area. Georg Simmel,[c] George H. Mead,[d] Edward Sapir[e] and John Dewey[f] were possibly the chief, early, definitive contributors to the study of human behavior as the phenomena of social interaction and communication. Harry Stack Sullivan,[g] Jurgen Ruesch and Gregory Bateson,[h] and Edwin A. Weinstein[i] are among other more recent workers who have not only added extensively to the body of theory but also have demonstrated the applicability of the theoretical concepts to clinical practice and to research problems.

It is of interest also to note that since the parts, characteristics and properties of individual "personality" have been derived from observations of behavior (and mainly from acculturated, or social behavior), a great part of the concepts and of the clinical lore accumulated by means of the older, dyadic, therapeutic methods can be, as it were, directly translated into the expanded form provided by the conceptual system of social interaction and communication. Thus, the theoretical framework of social psychiatry is not in conflict with the different psychiatric and psychological schools of thought which were elaborated during the first half of the century. It appears, rather, that our increasing clinical and theoretical knowledge has provided a base for more complex, but more precise, methods and formulations.

The result of these studies, i.e., combat psychiatry, has been demonstrated to be effective in a very high per cent of instances by longitudinal studies of the further course of men who received treatment and returned to duty. The great importance of maintaining a man's identity with the group to which he owed allegiance—that is, reference group—was demonstrated and also the importance of the consistency with which therapeutic and other personnel maintained the objective of the total organization. In the case of combat the objective was, of course, sharply defined and, consequently, there was remarkable stability and consistency of social communication. The studies on combat psychiatry also demonstrated the importance of implied messages. It was found, for example, that the label (e.g., the diagnosis) applied to persons carried a meaning which often determined recovery or chronicity. It was quite clear, also, that sending psychiatric patients to hospitals, thus confirming their fears, tended to fix the role of "illness" and so reduced the recovery rate very greatly.

Limiting the duration of treatment at different echelons carried the implication of the expectation of effectiveness of treatment and of recovery, both for the patients and for the psychiatric staff. Support of the staff in this respect was also found to be of importance since the staff expectations for the recovery and rehabilitation of the patients proved to be one of the most important factors for therapeutic success.

Certain major principles concerning the utilization of social factors in the treatment of neuropsychiatric syndromes stem from experiences in combat psychiatry. These principles have been increasingly applied during recent years to the work of the Mental Hygiene Consultation Service in various Army posts in the United States. Depending upon local situations, a variety of ways of applying these principles have been devised by the psychiatrists in charge. A general study of these different methods is now being conducted. Interest has further been generated by the successful application of these principles to the management of the problem of military offenders. The population of offenders sentenced to the disciplinary barracks has been sharply reduced in the past four years and the elimination of recidivists at an early stage has been accompanied by a higher rate of rehabilitation of certain groups of offenders.

In 1955 the Division of Neuropsychiatry, Walter Reed Army Institute of Research, developed plans to initiate an experimental ward for the application of principles of social psychiatry to the treatment of soldiers in their first psychotic episode. Colonel A. J. Glass was Chief of the Department of Psychiatry and under his direction Lt. Col. Kenneth L. Artiss was asked to take responsibility for the project. In a former volume, *The Symptom as Communication in Schizophrenia,* Lt. Col. Artiss and Lt. Col. Bruce Bushard, together with several social scientists, have described the general problems of military psychiatry and the longitudinal course of patients suffering their first schizophrenic episode during basic training. The consistency of the characteristics of the symptom from childhood through hospitalization and the manner in which the symptom is used to communicate the major social message of the patient before and during his illness was described and documented.

In the present volume Col. Artiss describes the process of establishing the ward and translating the general concepts of social psychiatry into everyday staff-staff and staff-patient interactions and into reliable sequences of interactions which could be eventually experienced as intimate human relationships. I have couched this statement in somewhat stilted (or somewhat esoteric) terms, not because I regard them as more accurate or adequate. Quite the contrary. It is rather that when one enters the reduced social world of schizophrenic communication, the primary need is to perceive and to answer in the overt and demonstrable here-and-now, which is not possible when the situation is seen through conventional linguistic constructs. It is necessary to see what goes on and what does it lead to if one wishes to decipher the major message of the patient and to respond understandably. This requires both the commitment of the staff to the objective of the ward and also security in this commitment sufficient to permit clear and accurate communication. It becomes necessary for the ward physician to identify sources of anxiety and to provide help in their solution for the staff as well as for the patients. It is of both practical and theoretical interest to note how closely the openness of the lines of communication (freedom and clarity of staff reports and discussion) correlate with the therapeutic effectiveness of the group organization on the ward.

It was not feasible to apply all the principles of social psychiatry developed in military psychiatry in the present investigation. Thus, the subjects were not treated in geographic proximity to their units in a non-hospital setting, but were evacuated to the Walter Reed General Hospital and were formally admitted as patients. In other respects, however, the progress of treatment was based on military psychiatric principles. For example, the duration of treatment was limited to six months; the objective was clearly defined, namely, return to duty; role responsibilities were set and documented; and contacts of the patients with activities off the ward were maintained on a military basis, not on the basis of hospital patients. It should be noted here that, as in other aspects of military psychiatry, knowledge of the military structure, the possibility of controlling certain aspects of it, the general recognition of adequate performance as the criterion for acceptance in the group, and the possibility of rapid and accurate measurements of this performance, make the study of the principles of social psychiatry and their application to particular therapeutic problems simpler than in most civilian settings.

One of the most significant and valuable contributions to psychiatric thinking presented in this volume comes in the chapter on the role of the physician. This contribution is the theoretical discussion—metaphorically presented as the "problem of naming." Does a person accept the name his group gives him with the mutual responsibilities and support implied or does he assert his social isolation by naming himself? Therapy with patients in schizophrenic episodes is an intensely personal experience whether or not conducted in the setting of the therapeutic community. When one insists on establishing reliable communication with a social isolate, one assumes the responsibility for a "struggle," if for no other reason than to demonstrate the reliability of human interest. Establishing communication with a person whose symbolic behavior seems to be like, but proves so unlike one's own, necessarily results in intense frustration and anxiety. Unless one is committed to the objective, it is much too easy to leave the isolate in his isolation and to direct one's attention to other matters, including diagnostic disposal and routine systems of therapy.

The work on the experimental ward for *milieu therapy* has not only provided much needed data on the biological course of the schizophrenic syndrome in military personnel and data on the identification of social factors and their utilization in therapy, but it has also provided the opportunity for conducting a series of studies of particular behaviors and functions. These have ranged from descriptive studies of group process to operant conditioning, measuring the changes in hormonal patterns and measuring autonomic reactivity. It is clear that once the clinical problem of the social structure of the ward is solved and the course of therapy is established, detailed research can be introduced and limited factors studied, both in their own right and also for their value as indicators or criteria of the course of therapy. The application of the principles on which this program of research has been based to the study and treatment of other syndromes, such as alcohol addiction, has been shown to be feasible. The research described here by Col. Artiss thus presents a basis for a variety of studies which are unique, in that historical, social, symbolic, communicative and experimentally evoked data are available for comparison, correlation and control.

David McK. Rioch, M.D.
Walter Reed Army Institute of Research
Washington, D.C.

REFERENCES

a. Kempf, E. J.: Psychopathology. St. Louis, C. V. Mosby & Co., 1921.
b. Sullivan, H. S.: Socio-psychiatric research: Its implications for the schizophrenia problem and for mental hygiene. Am. J. Psychiat. *10:* 977-991, 1931.
c. Wolff, K. H.: The Sociology of Georg Simmel. Glencoe, Ill., The Free Press, 1950.

d. Mead, G. H.: Mind, Self and Society. Chicago, Univ. of Chicago Press, 1934.

e. Sapir, E.: Language: An Introduction to the Study of Speech. New York, Harcourt, Brace & Co., 1921.

f. Dewey, J.: Human Nature and Conduct. New York, Henry Holt & Co., 1922.

g. Sullivan, H. S.: The Interpersonal Theory of Psychiatry. New York, W. W. Norton, 1953.

h. Ruesch, J., and Bateson, G.: Communication: The Social Matrix of Psychiatry. New York, W. W. Norton, 1951.

i. Weinstein, E. A.: Symbolic reorganization in brain injuries. *In* American Handbook of Psychiatry. S. Arieti, ed. New York, Basic Books, 1959.

Milieu Therapy
in
Schizophrenia

THE WARD AND ITS STAFF

The history of the development of a research milieu
therapy ward is outlined, together with a description of
the staff, its management, training, and its members'
problems in learning to work together.

HONORED AT BEING CHOSEN, pleased with the prospect of working closely with patients, a group of us opened an experimental
milieu therapy ward for the treatment of schizophrenic soldiers
early in July 1956. As a group, our encumbrances were few. We
possessed little research experience, a compensatory lack of
presuppositions regarding method, and membership in no particular "school" or fashion of psychiatric theory. Because of
our relative sophistication concerning Army culture as well as
Army social psychiatry, we were provided with considerable
autonomy and steady support from our superiors.

This report is being written three and one-half years later.
Much of the original optimism has been replaced by confidence
in the treatment method. Certain aspects of the original opti-
mistic attitude have been countered and neutralized by disap-
pointment as we have come to recognize that some patients do
not respond to our efforts in the time we have available. Presently, it appears that milieu therapy in an Army setting is indeed a useful adjunct to an over-all psychiatric hospital treatment program. It can restore the equilibrium of certain soldiers
suffering from their initial schizophrenic breakdown so that they
can return to duty successfully; and it possesses serendipity (i.e.,
it has an added advantage) in that the presence of such a unit
encourages the other hospital ward personnel to increased efforts
to better the welfare of *their* patients and by so doing raises the
level of patient care throughout the entire psychiatric unit.

From the beginning, we have recognized that the behavioral
sciences in general, and psychiatry in particular, are still in the

1

phase of exploratory research. Few generally accepted rules or methods have been laid down. Consequently, the research design called for the use of the tools of exploration; on-the-spot written reports, notes taken during an interview, tape-recorded interviews and "neutral" observers using systematic judgmental devices. Our findings will reflect the methods, of course, and must of necessity be couched in statements of a general nature, illustrative of trends and demonstrative of areas where more elaborate and systematic research is indicated.

The over-all general results were as follows:

63	Patients admitted to the ward
21	Patients eliminated from the study
	7 Not considered schizophrenic
	8 Transferred out with research design change
	6 Presently on ward
——	
42	Treated patients
27	Patients returned to duty—64 per cent

Since these results were obtained with no attention paid to criteria of treatability and by a pilot-project staff, it seems reasonable to expect that recovery figures in the vicinity of 80 per cent may be feasible with further knowledge relative to (1) selection of patients; (2) selection and training of staff members; (3) staff intercommunication systems; and (4) mores and values of patient group.

As a consequence of these encouraging results, further investigations are being undertaken. This report is aimed at providing an abbreviated account of our activities with the hope that our work may stimulate others to venture into milieu therapy and that our general body of knowledge will be increased thereby.

THE TREATMENT WARD

The Department of Neuropsychiatry at the Walter Reed General Hospital in Washington, D.C., is housed in a block of interconnected buildings set off from the main hospital proper and in the rear of the grounds. There are twelve similar wards, each designed to house twenty patients. The buildings are approximately 35 years old, air conditioned and well maintained.

One of the twelve wards was made available for research which would combine the psychiatric facilities of the hospital, then under the direction of Albert J. Glass, Colonel, MC, and those of the Division of Neuropsychiatry, Walter Reed Army Institute of Research, under the direction of David McK. Rioch, M.D. The ward differed from others only by the addition of a sound-proof recording room in one corner and the tape-recording equipment in a small adjacent room.

Beds were removed until only ten remained. The additional space was used to increase the bed-to-bed distance and for the establishment of two social corners on the ward. Both of these corners were comfortably furnished for sitting and talking and one had a radio and phonograph and record storage facility added. Draperies were added to the windows throughout and potted plants were placed upon each window sill. This relatively simple transformation completely altered the appearance and impression of the ward. To be sure, it remained a hospital ward, but the customary bleak, "institutional" atmosphere was markedly attenuated.

One of the two smaller rooms adjacent to the ward was furnished as a lounge and TV room, and the other with a ping-pong table which doubled as the group therapy conference table when a couple of sheets were thrown over it in imitation of the familiar family table cloth.

There is also a series of small offices opening onto the ward, such as the nurse's station, doctor's office, secretary's office, and social worker's office. Each is closed off by its door, but always in reach of the patient so that he may meet with its occupant via the social convention of knocking on his door. Patients' clothing and baggage are kept in a similar room, available when needed.

A brief description of activities appears elsewhere.[6] For those who have not seen it, this section will be repeated here:

The patients are up at 6:30 a.m., shave themselves, wash, breakfast and complete their daily details (chores) in time for formal ward rounds at 8:30. The details comprise the ward housekeeping. They are managed entirely by a patient-government group. This organization elects its own officers and meets at its own will, particularly to plan its responsibilities, make recommendations to the staff, plan picnics, trips, etc., and in general, provide its own internal patient-group management.

Ward rounds are traditional, the staff accompanying the doctor while problems are discussed and plans for the day are made. The doctor asks each patient to decide on the timing of his individual psychotherapy sessions and this aspect of the day is also planned at this time.

Following rounds, the group gathers in the conference room around the table, with morning coffee and "smokes" for the group therapy session. The doctor conducts, the remainder of the staff "sitting in" as observers, to answer specific questions if needed and to gain further information concerning patient attitudes and problems.

Following this hour, the patients and technicians go to the gymnasium for an hour of almost any kind of gymnasium sport to be wished, followed by a shower and, shortly thereafter, the midday meal. Incidentally, all meals are taken in a large dining room with all other patients from the neuropsychiatric building.

After 15 to 20 minutes free time, the patient group goes to an occupational therapy section, well equipped and staffed for considerable individual attention. During this period, the technician staff meets with the doctor and nurse for training, to plan therapeutic maneuvers, to exchange ideas and information about their relationships with patients, and in general, to abet staff communication.

Next hour, the technicians are with the patient group again, this time at the swimming pool for games and exercise. This activity finishes at 2:30 p.m. and the afternoon relaxation period begins.

Certain patients leave the ward at this time on a grounds pass. These privileges, while ultimately approved by the doctor, are nevertheless managed by the patient-government group. Individual psychotherapy sessions are usually scheduled at this time; when more are necessary, the patient may be held back from other activities. Another doctor-staff meeting takes place at the end of the day with the evening shift.

After the evening meal, movies and dances are available at regular intervals. During this period, the busy-scheduled day is behind and concentration is upon the promotion of "bull-sessions" and opportunities to "talk things over" with the trained staff. Without formal direction or design, many therapeutic relationships develop during this time.

THE STAFF

In Army hospitals, the doctor in charge of a ward is designated as Ward Officer. He is placed on official orders as such, giving him the requisite legal authorization to carry out his responsibilities. During the reported period, the writer was Ward Officer for two one-year periods. For the remainder of the time he was in a supervisory capacity. Three Walter Reed psychiatry residents and a post-residency civilian psychiatrist on two-year Army duty functioned as Ward Officers for varying periods ranging from four to six months.

Although these young psychiatrists made genuine contributions, there will be a paucity of material concerning them in this report. They universally reported their learning experience as high in personal gratification, but felt that they did not really begin to "get the hang of" the problems of running such a ward until the fifth month.

The nurse assigned to the project, Major Charlotte R. Rodeman, ANC, had in common with me the factor, "career Army." She had already demonstrated capabilities in handling a wide variety of neuropsychiatric nursing assignments, including that of teacher and author.[101] We had not met prior to the assignment. She went to work with a will, became and has remained my strong professional support throughout the entire project.

Her very important contributions to the ward operation included a tight and clear-cut management of the staff organization. [There is a subtle but most vital point here that should be made clear for the benefit of those who have not had post-war Army Medical Service experience. Following World War II, civilian physicians serving two years of obligatory duty in the Army were vociferous in many complaints. One of these was "too many administrative duties." This led to a change of policy in which the medical technicians (at times known as ward boys, aides, corpsmen, practical nurses, etc.) were assigned as the responsibility of the nursing service. Since this time, the hospital ward nurse has directed them in their duties, time schedules, has "hired and fired," recommended for promotion, recommended for disciplinary action, etc. For a time there was some dissension, the young soldier in the capacity of medical aide stating a conventional resentment about "taking orders from a woman." This complaint has apparently gone out of style and is now rarely, if ever, heard. On the whole, the system has been effective.] The nurse handled the vast majority of administrative problems herself and conferred with me only concerning those in which she required backing or for some reason was uncertain as to her next move.

Her major contribution to the therapeutic effort was an earnest and sincere attempt to keep abreast of what was going on through the use of her already excellent communication talents. Her courage in asking the question that everyone else had avoided, bringing the hidden issues out into the open where they could be discussed and persistently seeking a realistic solution to the patients' needs was so great as to make her an indispensable part of the therapeutic team.

"Neuropsychiatric technician" is Army nomenclature for that vitally important person to hospital psychiatry, the attendant. Over the years of dealing with hospitalized patients, like my fellow psychiatrists, I have been overwhelmed with the magnitude of the need for therapy as contrasted with the short supply of therapists. Many times I have been deeply impressed with the talents, insight and understanding exhibited by individual attendants. However, the attendant has a large field of responsibility, little training and no real opportunity to use what talents he may possess, so that what attendant-patient therapeutic relationships I have seen have been exceptions, rather than the expected. I found in this assignment an opportunity to test my hypothesis; that there was a gold mine of therapeutic ability in the attendant, could it only be exploited.

The technicians for the ward were drawn from those assigned through regular channels to the Walter Reed General Hospital. I had no selection other than the authority not to accept those few I thought unsuitable. The supply was scant and my rejections negligible. By this token, however, there was some small element of selection. No one was asked to work on the project without his full acceptance of an assignment to the milieu therapy ward in lieu of assignment elsewhere and none were kept who did not wish to stay.

Concerning these men, the nurse reports as follows:

During the period of the study there were 33 technicians assigned to the ward. Ages at time of assignment ranged from 20 to 35. Education ranged from completion of elementary school to completion of the Baccalaureate degree in various fields including business administration, economics, experimental psychology and anthropology. Previous experience in psychiatry ranged from none at all to 14 years in this field, most of the experience having been in Army hospitals with some in State or Federal institutions.

Three technicians assigned during this time were civilians, the remainder were military in the grades from private up to and including sergeant and specialist five. There was no criterion as to race. Of the total number assigned ten were Negro and the remaining Caucasian.

At the end of three years, four of the men originally assigned were still on duty. Of these, one was a civilian, the other three Regular Army men, one sergeant and two specialists five.

Twenty-two men left the ward during the period of study for the following reasons: Ten men completed their Army enlistment, three were assigned overseas, one was assigned to another hospital in the United States, one (psychology major) was assigned to the audio-visual aid section, Walter Reed Army Institute of Research. One man was transferred because of overstrength on the ward and the remaining six were transferred because of inability to adjust.

Of the six who left the ward because of inability to adjust, three (two civilian) requested the transfer because of their own increasing anxiety in the situation. Three were transferred at the request of the doctor and nurse because of frequent difficulties in their relationships with the patient and technician groups.

THE SHAKEDOWN VOYAGE

One of the major problems facing me as I opened the ward was staff training. Not knowing if it could be done, I was to build a small group of strangers into a therapeutic unit. A simple plan called for spending an hour each day with the technicians from two of the three shifts, 7:00 a.m.—3:00 p.m. and 3:00 p.m.—11:00 p.m. Noting that this would take ten hours in my weekly schedule, I felt that I could not afford it and eventually compromised on four such meetings each week with each shift, a total of eight hours weekly.

Incidentally, the design called for each staff person, including the nurse, to write daily reports concerning interaction with each patient. These reports were available to the doctor each morning as he came to work. This system was put into effect as an attempt to counteract the doctor's proverbial innocence about "what really goes on" during the other twenty-three hours that he does not see his patient.

The meetings, or "tech conferences" as they came to be called, took place in the doctor's office, chairs being brought in as needed. The nurse attended whenever possible and all technicians on duty, save one who remained on the ward with the patients. The door was left slightly ajar in case any help should be needed by the lone technician. Only in rarest incidents of extreme tension was it necessary for a technician to leave this meeting to help out on the ward proper.

The reports had been read by the doctor and he was by this token already filled in to a degree concerning the general atmosphere of the various technician-patient problems of the moment. Questions about elements of the reports provided a convenient opening for the doctor to use in beginning a discussion period.

With such structure, one might have anticipated that these sessions would have gone well. They did not.

As a matter of fact, they went so poorly that, had it not been for the encouragement of the nurse, I would have given them up in hopeless frustration twice in the first five months. Few of the technicians were neophytes and several came with considerable prior experience. Apparently their customary ways of dealing with the doctor had been to greet him on his arrival and note his departure, and very little else. Here, not only were they writing reports—with the accompaniment of the usual concern that anyone has when he must place his actions and ideas in permanent form—but furthermore, they were asked to expand verbally in many ways. Their response to this anxious situation was to withdraw into (or remain in) a conventional politeness. They were prompt, interested, willing, alert—but they didn't say anything.

I tried various methods of getting them involved, techniques that had always worked in groups before. They responded only as long as necessary and again reverted to their customary role, "sitting at the feet of the master, waiting for pearls of wisdom to drop from his lips."

Thoroughly frustrated by this ridiculous situation, I was one day pacing the empty ward trying to think of a solution when the nurse persuaded me to talk to her about what was bothering me—as if she didn't know. Before we had finished, it had been necessary for her to outline point for point the entire training method to which these technicians had been previously subjected. She described their customary role of listening to lectures, seeing practical demonstrations and passing tests. Because I was doing "training" this was what they expected. "You must realize," she explained, "that they've never *really* talked to a doctor before."

So, I kept on trying. Finally, after five months, the technicians, one by one, gradually began to talk to me as if I were another human being. Of course, it goes without saying, that as they did, their data became more reliable, their interaction with patients more meaningful and for the first time we began to make some predictable sense out of what was going on.

This experience went a long way towards clarifying for me one central explanation for the fact that the psychiatric aid is so seldom used as a therapeutic agent. What overburdened ward psychiatrist can afford 30 to 40 hours a month for five months to do the necessary initial training? How often has one tried as I did and failed because he could no longer afford the time or because he had no one available to help him see the problem?

THE NEW COMMUNICATION SYSTEM

With the removal of the block in communication between the technicians and the senior staff, a whole new "world" of information became available. Most of this new world was composed of problems with patients which the staff customarily keeps to itself. For a time, these new data threatened to inundate the entire unit. In retrospect the sense of being overwhelmed was probably connected to the fact that no previous experience or training had prepared us to deal with it.

For purposes of presentation, these problems have been artificially separated into four areas; distrust, over-or-under-expectancy, general tension level and repetitive small annoyances. They will be discussed in that order.

Distrust

The most serious staff problem and one which still keeps recurring from time to time is that relative to degree of trust or reliability.

Briefly, what happened was this: As it became safely possible for the staff to express its feelings concerning the patients, a central theme developed, "I have been deceived." Person after person, whether belonging essentially to the treatment or investigative group, brought in a similar story. He found himself angry or annoyed with a patient, or a member of his family. In trying to locate the source of his annoyance, he found that his attitude stemmed from an experience in which he had felt tricked. More specifically, the patient or family member had told him something which later turned out to be quite false,*

---

* "False" when used denotatively is relatively innocent and descriptive, but its connotations are highly charged. The connotative aspect, "the lie by a liar" has caused no end of difficulty for me as well as my staff. First, it implies intent to deceive and by that token has legal-moral implications. Secondly, it carries the notion of deliberate-malicious. Thirdly, it is fundamentally distasteful for a psychiatric person to be asked to deal with such a (to him) tremendously condensed and oversimplified concept as guilt versus innocence. However, to substitute "distorted" would be to miss the emotional impact with which "false" is connotatively accompanied.

and this discovery induced the conventional response of anger at being deceived. Examples range all the way from the pica-yune to the grotesque. Patient reports that a picture on his bedside stand is his girl friend. Staff member later discovers that his closest contact with her was to print a publicity picture of her in a photo-shop where he worked. Two patients report one to three years at a university, (Columbia and McGill in this series) and when they discover this will be investigated, reveal the invention. Patient's mother reports that he did quite well in school and had no problems, then changes this (when the investigator is in the city and plans to contact the school) to "he was nothing but trouble in school since fourteen and his grades grew steadily worse until he had to leave," which was confirmed. Patient reports self as highly honest, ethical, until his sister reveals their four years of teamwork in stealing from stores and subway magazine stands.

Remembering that period, it would seem that we had been prepared for a certain type of distortion; the delusional, hallu-cinatory, disoriented distortions were part of our experience. None of us had been able previously to spend enough time with the schizophrenic patient to come to know him more simply as a person and by that token to become aware of the many other areas in which he distorted the world about him to fit into his fantasics. We had to learn that there is a rela-tionship between "I went to Columbia for three years" and "I am great. I just know it. I am great."

As the staff was struggling to digest this new and unexpected aspect of increasing knowledge concerning its patients, further new facets of the problem appeared. We found ourselves react-ing to the deceptions we were discovering with a feeling of dis-trust and a vague accusatory attitude towards the patient group. As we were trying to find out what the "facts" were from our patients, it was inevitable that our aims did indirectly accuse them of the possibility of insincerity—whatever we may have said. During the same time, the patients were feeling exactly the same way about the staff, finally "spilling it out" in a flood during one group therapy session in which they pointed out that they "have come to feel that the technicians frequently approach them, endeavor to start a conversation *in order to have something to write on their reports,* and by inference, of course, not to engage in a genuine person-to-person human relationship."— (Doctor's diary).

Only later did we hear case reports from Otto Allen Will describing this same type of phenomenon in the dyadic therapy relationship. Still later, he presented further evidence in his magnificent Frieda Fromm-Reichmann Memorial Lecture, "Human Relatedness and the Schizophrenic Reaction."[148]

This series of experiences served eventually to provide a more realistic model for use in considering distrust. It has become useful to consider it in terms applicable to interaction, rather than to a person or group. Rather than, "I distrust him," or "He cannot be trusted," it appears to be more meaningful to see the phenomena in terms of, "We distrust each other." Rephrased, it could be, "Distrust is a factor in the relationship that exists between us."

At the risk of belaboring the point, "distrust" is better understood as part of the communication system that can be established between a staff group and a patient group, rather than by being attributed to either party as sole possessor (Fig. 1).

Recognition of this factor apparently allows a given techni-

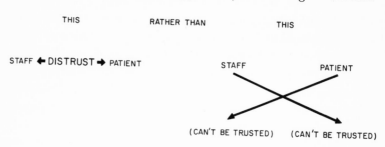

Fig. 1

cian to talk with a given patient in terms of the immediate present, "the way we distrust each other." In this sense, it becomes "our problem," and by that token remarkably different from "your problem." From the standpoint of the technician, it allows him the prerogative of noting "similarity" between himself and his patient, rather than requiring him to constantly note the "difference factors" (delusions, hallucinations, etc.).

Over-or-Under-Expectancy

Consistently throughout this study, the patients who were going to respond satisfactorily signaled the eventual outcome with a change of behavior during the interval between 60 and 90 days of hospitalization. In each case this change was marked by a relatively sudden decrease in negativism, however it may have been characteristically expressed; this was replaced by an increased degree of cooperative or "friendly" behavior.

Two to three months of negativism, ranging from the provoking to the dangerous, is a very real problem for the staff. Technicians are discouraged by constant rebuffs from a patient, dismayed by their inabilities to "get through to him" and by their own feelings of frustration.

One aspect of this problem centers around the staff's expectancies. It works earnestly towards helping the patient to find a more workable social method of living. This means that the patient must change. When he resists, it is all too easy to see him as "being deliberately frustrating." When his behavior is so categorized by the staff, there is little possibility for him to make his way unaided out of the impasse which develops.

A majority of the conferences between the doctor and his staff were taken up with this basic problem. No one general solution presented itself and, in several cases, the impasse remained just that and no substantial progress was made. In those cases with successful outcome, two main factors seemed relevant: (1) The staff expects too much sincerity too early and (2) the staff finds itself treating the patient like a thing (a schizophrenic) and not as a person.

Expecting too much sincerity of response too soon was handled with the staff by referring its members to their lives outside the ward. When they were persuaded to take a changed perspective, they could see that they too, faced with a new working acquaintance, situation or potential friend did in fact take two or three months to check out the situation. This allowed for the beginnings of a formulation which went something like this: Friendship is related to a sense of increased acceptance and this is related to the presentation of increasingly personal information about oneself.

Using this simple and acceptable framework, it was then possible to illustrate that in order for one person to present increasingly intimate (sincere in this case) data concerning himself he must possess some certainty about how this information will be received. If, for example, he strongly suspects that it will meet with scorn and derision, he will weigh this factor and probably refrain from taking the chance. Furthermore, he learns that it takes time for two people to "sound out" each other and come to that agreeable relationship which they call friendship. He learns that he must not expect "sincerity" from a person he has just met. If this is generally true and we then consider the schizophrenic patient in Sullivan's terms as a person who has given up hope of being loved (appreciated or respected) and who remains only interested in security operations, then certainly the expectancy of sincerity should be lessened.

The working technician knows that he cannot accept "craziness" as a means of relating to the patient. At the same time, he may be presented with very little else. When he can, however, come to tolerate the "craziness" while he is alert for evidences of humanity which he can accept, his position is improved. Many technicians found the following recipe helpful: "We can accept the patient without accepting his behavior. There is more to a patient than just what he says or does."

The factor of under-expectancy we customarily came to discuss in terms of "treating him like a patient." The models used for illustration were derived from two common experiences. The first is known to every psychiatric aide with even a minimum of experience. When reminded, he will immediately recall an experience which customarily occurs within a few hours of a new patient's arrival, when the patient turns to the nearby aide and inquires, "Why am I here?" The school-trained response is, "You are here because you are sick." To which the patient either replies "Oh," or tries to find out what is meant by "sick" or immediately disagrees with a stout disclaimer.

The other common experience is that of being physically struck by a patient. The nurse reports a discussion between a technician and me following such an incident:

Doctor: "Did it make you angry?"
Technician: "No."
Doctor: "Why not?"
Technician: "Because you don't get angry at a patient."

Both such examples have been useful in bringing to light the demeaning quality inherent in these attitudes. In the first instance, the person who replies to such a loaded question as, "Why am I here?" with such a response does at the same time tacitly accept the inference that the patient is in fact so defective as to be unaware, despite the clearly known fact that of all people in the world the patient was the only actor present at all of the scenes which led to his "being here" on a closed psychiatric ward. To wit: he is the person in possession of the most information; the technician asked is in possession of little, if any. The question of whether or not the patient can integrate the knowledge he possesses is another matter, but the technician who replies, "Why do you ask me?" is at least keeping the subject open.

"You don't get angry with a patient," I am informed, is fairly frequent instruction to both nurses and aides. Apparently, it is often taken literally to the point of making the staff person appear "wooden and cold" to the patient. The nurse tells me that she recalls instruction to this effect and "You are not supposed to show your feelings and so you don't talk about them —and they come out in other ways." In general, experience supports her view and one of the other ways is quite probably neatly disguised in a message to the patient, "You're not important enough to affect me."

Discussed in terms such as these, the phenomena do appear to become clarified for the technician and a more rational method for him to relate with his patient becomes available. Being able to reply, "Of course, I don't like it if you hit me. But why do you do it?" provides for further interchange.

General Tension Level

The type of approach used in training the staff, providing as it did new avenues for communication as well as a wealth of information not always easy to assimilate, also led to some interesting hypotheses. One of these was helpfully clarified in a discussion with Henry W. Brosin* (personal communication) when we were fortunate enough to have him as a visitor on the ward. It goes as follows:

In an operating group, the degree of intimacy in communication will be inversely related to the anxiety or tension level existing in the group.

Example: A will confide in B to a degree dependent upon his anticipation of feedback support, e.g., he is more likely to discuss his intimate thoughts and experiences if he anticipates a response such as, "Yes, go on," than he will be if he anticipates, "That's silly." Furthermore, A will explore B's attitudes X times to test the probability of positive response before he advances further.

_____
* Director, Western Psychiatric Institute, University of Pittsburgh.

When a respondent is operating at a low anxiety level and/or in a climate of low-level anxiety, e.g., demonstrates comfort, ease, confidence, he will find it easier to tolerate and accept the ideas and experiences of another different from his own.

Although we recognized that such a broad and general theory could not be adequately and rigorously tested in our situation, we have accepted it as having a priori validity for the purpose of this treatment study. It is peculiarly appropriate to a milieu therapy unit, since it calls upon the doctor to pay unusual attention to the group-anxiety level of his staff. It suggests to him that if his staff's anxiety level is above some critical level, it cannot be useful, tolerant and accepting of its patients. This issue will be discussed at some length in a later chapter.

Operationally, I have found that I must spend approximately 40 percent of my time with the staff in order to help it in maintaining a low-enough tension level so as to be useful to the patient-group. This, of course, seems like a huge block of a therapist's time, and as a matter of fact it is. However, I have found it essential to the establishment of such a satisfactory milieu for the patient as will allow him to express his "secrets," fantasies, wishes. And, of course, I operate upon the tacit assumption that it is advisable and helpful for him to do so.

In addition to the technician conferences, the nurse was seen individually for an hour each week, as was the social worker and any other professional person engaged in research concerning the patients. The ward secretary was seen daily, either during a period of dictation or for planning the day's appointments. Further, it became necessary to find one hour per week for a general administrative staff conference, attended by everyone.

Such an elaborate system of conferences and discussions seems preposterous on the face of it, in a group whose sole responsibility is the treatment of a small handful of schizophrenic soldiers. It could be easily derogated as a "Parkinson's Law" sort of effect in which a small bureaucracy solidifies itself by finding new duties whose sole function is the continuation of the bureaucracy as such. Critics might also suggest that this 40 percent of the doctor's and staff's time might well be reduced to 10 percent and the remainder given to patients.

Indeed, no one could be more empathetic with these critics than I. Superficially, it doesn't seem reasonable that a doctor should be required to spend so much time with a group of normals, just to help them keep functioning. However, each step in this direction has been necessary in order to keep the communication system sufficiently free from distortions that it could deal effectively with patients.

Small Annoyances Which May Pile Up

When any one person on the staff loses effective communication with another, both are so distressed by the situation as to become virtually useless to the total effort. These persons usually find a way of getting their discomfort to the attention of others and sooner or later it comes to the doctor. By the time it does, it has usually reached the "not speaking to each other" stage. At this point, each will describe the other's behavior as insufferable, in language containing a high incidence of the projection mechanism. The doctor, in consideration of the total effort, must take ameliorative steps. The most successful maneuvers for me were ones whose eventual aim was a restoration of the communication between the two warring parties. At no time was it necessary to put the two of them in one room and lock the door for a while, but some authoritative duress was essential at times.

When some form of communication was again established, the parties improved their perspectives concerning each other and revised the distorted images to correspond somewhat more accurately to the other person, now again a communicant. The typical result was a changed working relationship, often involving compromise, which allowed the parties to more adequately tolerate each other, accompanied by a sense of relief on all sides (for everyone in the group knows when two of its members are quarreling) and a return to the urgent job at hand.

No attempt was made to compare the incidence of intra-staff dissension with that of other dissimilar working groups. One has the impression, however, that the ability of the schizophrenic patient to arouse anxiety in others is indeed a relevant variable and that this factor materially affects the incidence of intra-staff disorder. Furthermore, patients become remarkably adept at sensing such possibilities and engage from time to time in surprisingly complex strategies aimed at setting one person on the staff against another. Once again, effective intra-staff communication appeared to be the real remedy. When two persons could confront each other with dissimilar reactions from a particular patient, then and then only did his strategy become evident. "He told you that about me? Well, I'll be damned, he told me thus and so about you." "What can he be up to?"

When a staff member felt distress of such nature as to force him to seek treatment, he was referred elsewhere. I was careful not to allow any member of the staff to consider that he had engaged me as a therapist. I served only as a source of referral and would see to it that this matter was handled satisfactorily, beyond which point I would not go. I wished to make it explicit that my staff was a working unit in my eyes and that we were in the business of treating patients, not each other. Perhaps an explanation of this strategy is in order, particularly for the reader who is relatively new in psychiatry. It simply develops out of experience over the years with those many persons who come into ancillary positions in the psychiatric world secretly hoping that they can obtain treatment for themselves, on the sly, as it were, without anyone's knowing what they are doing. I have learned that groups in hospitals and clinics do at times engage in the titillating fancy that they are treating each other. The only result I have ever witnessed is increased anxiety, leading at times to disruptive behavior.

Another potential disaster area can be avoided by the doctor if he will recognize early how a staff may come to use psychiatry jargon as a "polite" system of disguised "name calling." Mem-

bers tend to find certain aspects of another's behavior irritating
or annoying in some respect and resort to such phrases as "My,
but you're paranoid today," when what they really mean is,
"Damn you, I don't like your attitude towards me." Again, the
parties are better able to find for themselves compatible working arrangements if they can talk to each other clearly enough
to find out what is irritating. "Name calling," even if disguised
in scientific terminology, is no doubt a derivative of the label-
ing or nosological stance; aimed at placing the irritant at a distance—from which understanding then becomes impossible.

At times, it would appear that the doctor must function as a
"preventive maintenance man" alert to what may get out of
order in his staff, in order that he may be able to "head it off"
rather than find himself faced with an incident which is already
a *fait accompli*. Staffs of persons working under tension do indeed bring along with them many a disruptive potential, in
addition to those already mentioned, such as competitiveness
and that misery which is often dubbed "sibling rivalry," for
example. It is simply not politic for the doctor to turn his back
and hope that these factors will disappear.

GROUP THERAPY

Group therapy, rarely used in the treatment of acutely
psychotic persons, is described, along with the accompanying attitudes of staff and patients, some examples of
sessions and an objective analysis.

HERE WE SAW an opportunity to further test the use of group
therapy in a population of acutely schizophrenic persons. The
most important issue, of course, was the question as to whether,
in this setting, it could be done at all. Fortunately, we are living in an era of increased interest in social psychiatry, as well
as one which encourages research endeavors. What might have
been considered extreme or radical twenty years ago is acceptable and feasible today.

A group gathered together, ostensibly for reasons of therapy,
can, of course, assume a variety of arrangements. The physical
arrangement of the group will influence the group's activities.
Some of these factors have been explored by Wilmer[150] during
the period that he has devoted to investigating the influences
of the staff upon its patients. In terms of communication potential, Matthew D. Parrish* (personal communication) has
suggested that probably the ideal would be a small group of
persons sitting in a circle holding hands, so that the interac-
tion-nuances of feeling could be increased. Parrish suggests
that a type of opposite could be a group sitting around a room
at widely spaced intervals, in which case each member would
have a greater opportunity for "privacy" and consequently
greater selection of that portion of himself which he wishes to
present to the group. Parrish has done considerable exploratory work with groups in a community clinic setting and we
hope he will publish some of his findings.

---

* Assistant Chief, Psychiatry & Neurology Consultants Division, Surgeon
General's Office, U. S. Army.

21

Fig. 2

I started the group sitting in comfortable "easy chairs" in a small circle surrounding a small low table for ash trays, etc. I was comfortable, possibly because I liked my chair, but the staff apparently was not, and soon persuaded me to move the group to another room where we could all sit around a table. The table used is a standard ping-pong table over which hospital sheets are draped *a la* the conventional household dining room table (Fig. 2) around which many a conference has presumably taken place in the families from which our patients emanate. This setting, accompanied by the morning's second cup of coffee and smokes, has become traditional to the ward and is now the place where conferences of all types take place, including the weekly administrative staff meeting. There is indeed an air of formality mixed with the "homey" quality, possibly related to its distant cousin, the "conference table," around which business, professional and diplomatic decisions are made.

Each patient is expected to attend and is so invited by the doctor during the ward rounds which precede his first session. At intervals throughout the study, certain patients have demonstrated a variety of resistances to even sitting at the table, let alone contributing. Since one of the major goals for the staff is exploring the patients' social disabilities, such behavior becomes an issue and remains one until it is resolved, in favor of the patient's regular attendance. At times, patients will announce their unwillingness to attend previous to the meeting in an attempt to test out the predictability of the situation. Such an announcement is treated as an invitation rather than a rebuff and the staff has learned to respond, seeking out the patient in an attempt to elucidate "what's bothering him" or what he is attempting to accomplish. Usually, his "announcement" has been merely one aspect of a generalized opposition to the staff, which, when we have been able to understand it, has been designed to arouse staff concern in this area so that it would not notice some other area which the patient was trying to protect via this diversionary maneuver. With other patients, it has been used apparently to test other parameters, being resolved for example by a special trip out to the ward by the nurse, or failing that, by the doctor. Sometimes it appears to disguise such a simple (but fundamental) question as, "Do you really want me?" or "Do you really mean what you say?"

Far more common is the patient who stalks out in high dudgeon when some aspect of the discussion goes against his wishes or plans—and the rare patient who quietly walks out without a word, usually having become quite anxious concerning something being discussed. It is now the custom that one of the staff members quietly gets up and goes along with the patient, giving him the opportunity to ventilate, trying to elucidate further the source of the disruptive behavior and, of course, by inference insisting upon the staff's right to know about its patients.

On the whole, maintaining the attendance of the patients was not a problem of great significance. It probably correlates positively with the over-all milieu attitude as seen by the patient. Going to group therapy is one of the standard operations, the more standard it becomes, the more "unheard of" becomes the idea of not attending. Further, it has certain traditions, one of which is that its daily occurrence came into being at the behest of a previous group of patients who had been dissatisfied with the three-times-weekly schedule and requested more hours.

ATTITUDE OF STAFF

It has also become custom that the nurse and technician staff attend the group therapy sessions. There are many reasons for having them present and few for leaving them out. Probably the most important single factor of benefit is the opportunity for staff members to increase their understanding of patients' attitudes and behavior, the reason they were asked to attend in the first place. Coming, as the sessions do, in the morning, they frequently set the tone for the day and provide openings for many discussions to follow later between individuals.

Staff people sit at the table when there is room and have their coffee and smokes with the patients. Ordinarily, they are observers, rarely participants. From time to time they are concerned in or with the discussion and chime in, participating whenever they feel a need to clarify an incident or experience. Their presence further adds conviction to one of the cardinal unwritten rules which govern the ward, "There are things that may not be done here, but there is nothing that may not be talked about." In this, as well as many other subtle ways, the message goes out to the patient that it *is* a hospital ward, a place where one's private self is the legitimate subject of investigation and treatment, a place where reticence and shame do not properly belong.

The therapist is, of course, the central figure. It would appear that staff members gain increasing security in their own operations with patients from seeing him in operation, in part at least by using him as model, and also some increased gratification for their deep yearnings to be a real part of the treatment procedure and to "know what is going on."

There are times when topics under discussion appear to arouse some anxiety in staff members, but these have been relatively rare. They have caused no lasting disruptions in this group. On the whole, group therapy is apparently one of the "don't miss it" activities insofar as the staff is concerned.

ATTITUDES OF PATIENTS

The wide range of patient responses to the group therapy situation cannot easily be described, since it ranged from week-long silences to the apparent opposite of dominating the session via monologue for long periods. One patient remained absent from the table, although hovering nearby, for sixty days. Many others used every minute; first to enter, last to leave, as it were.

The silent session is a phenomenon worthy of comment. Several have occurred in which I allowed an unbroken silence for the full hour. Within about ten minutes, many members will have signaled their discomfort through various means such as squirming in chairs, excessive smoking, looking downward and avoiding others' eyes. In general, this is followed by an electric tension which appears to pervade the entire group—as if they had decided that they would not talk and were going to maintain this stance whatever the cost in tension. At times it would appear like a group phenomenon, with some tentative organization. Such a thesis, however, was never established as a fact. Rather, later explanations would be more consistent with that of a group of persons operating as individuals, grouped mainly by chance. Such tentative explanations by observers as, "They are determined to defeat you in a struggle of silence," were also not confirmed.

One such group is considered in the following excerpt from a doctor's diary:

For several sessions now, the group has shown an interest in its own silent periods and the evaluation of these. It gradually worked itself out this morning to be a fairly general feeling that group members were hesitant about bringing up personal problems for discussion because of a feeling that this would result in judgments by other group members.

The theme of being judged is not new, and if it serves any purpose at all, it is to accent the previous theme of a feeling of not being understood by other group members. I cannot yet evaluate the fact that the feeling of not being understood by the staff here, either individually or collectively, has not been mentioned. One can only postulate that it is either not a very important problem, or it is such a tremendous problem that it cannot even be discussed.

The members seem quite serious, interested, and responsive in talking about their feelings of being misunderstood, but at the same time it must be noted that spontaneity and enthusiasm are most obvious for their absence.

Within a week's time, the diary contains the following:

This morning, the group completely, thoroughly and entirely reversed its customary procedure in that there was no waiting or hesitancy whatsoever, and ——— acted as spokesman for the group to say that they had been talking about sex and that they wanted to talk about it this morning.

They approached the area with some hesitancy and it soon became evident that one of the big problems involved their feelings of concern about discussing these matters in front of the nurse. They discussed feelings about her from the realistic point of view as well as hinting broadly at their fantasies. Several expressed concern that if they did bring up the subject with her, they would (1) evoke her dislike; (2) appear themselves so naive as to be in danger of "being laughed at"; (3) possibly insult her or hurt her feelings because of the danger that they might express some of their private thinking to the effect that she probably had sex problems of her own—"She doesn't let you forget for a minute that she's a woman . . . she tries to act like a man around here especially with the technicians . . . she won't let them be themselves and always has to express her authority over them . . . even when she goes out to the gym to play boys' games with us, she's still a woman," etc.

There was a brief attempt at interpretation and comparison of this with their fantasies and projections about their mothers, but apparently other matters were too pressing to continue this. I sensed a feeling of urgency in the group as if they felt they must quickly discuss this whole area and get it over with before the nurse returned. (She is away from the ward today.)

In rapid succession they scanned such topics as the proper age for sex indoctrination by parents, pre-marital sexual intercourse, feelings and ideas about masturbation and ended up with a prolonged discussion of homosexuality with ——— (a figure then prominent in the news) as the jumping-off place. They raised such questions as whether homosexuality was inborn or learned and including the question as to whether homosexuals should be punished. ——— and ——— volunteered that they should not and ——— offering without further comment, that they should be punished.

The session ran smoothly and spontaneously throughout. I had no difficulty in referring the questions back to their origins and my attitude alone, as well as cooperative interest, have perhaps allowed the topic a certain aura of respectability and freedom for future discussion.

This type of experience has been repeated frequently enough by this time to disabuse me of the oversimplified construction that they as a group were demonstrating simple hostility by not talking. Many times, when the tension was high, it has seemed so, but further understanding—whenever it was possible—has not failed to bring more meaningful explanations to light.

Overt hostility in group sessions presents a very real challength to therapeutic aims, just as it does elsewhere in the ward life of the patient. What makes it such a challenge is its persistence. The staff views with considerable difficulty in comprehension the patient who can be consistently nasty and insulting for prolonged periods—*without a break*. One such patient dominated the sessions daily for well over a month with a clever and astonishingly well organized attack on the motives of myself and my staff, using as his principal bludgeon the "brainwashing" accusation.

There are several points of view from which this problem may be considered. Classically, it may be seen as a type of "resistance" to therapy. We have so considered it elsewhere[5] and see it as an excellent diversionary maneuver by which means the patient forcibly directs emphasis on some area of his choosing in order to circumvent either his or his audience's noticing some other material which he wishes to avoid. At this point let me emphasize that my efforts are confined to reporting as best I may what happened, without recourse to models which require the use of such terms as "repression," "denial," "unconscious," etc.

Harold Searles[117] has considered the matter of the patient's attempt to drive the therapist crazy. Briefly comparing notes with him, I found that his observations appear to have remarkable cogency when applied to some of the operations of my schizophrenic patients seen as a group in a therapy situation. Certainly this patient was expert. Certainly he did dominate the sessions and take them where he wished them to go. Certainly he took valuable time that could have been devoted to other patients' problems. Certainly he "ran the sessions" that would appear to be mine to run. Certainly he was loud. He furnished me with every plausible reason to throw him out.

At the same time, he was also expressing another aspect of himself, a clever, ingenious small boy who braved the hazards of authority with considerable courage, and most important of all, humor. In "taking me apart piece by piece" he paid me a great compliment that he and I understood. In so directing his caustic comments principally to me, he could avoid harshly dissecting some other members of the staff who might not have stood it so well. It was part of a loud drama in which he was the leading actor, thoroughly enjoying his own performance. Never had he played to such an attentive audience. As understanding of this facet of his personality gradually infused through the staff, his performance became desperate, increasing in fervor until the day when the group therapy hour was not enough and he followed me to my office door. He shouted louder and louder, reaching deep into his vocabulary for terrible names to call me. As his intensity reached a peak, he shouted his false teeth out, caught them in his hands before they had fallen to the floor and kept right on with his tirade for a few minutes more.

By this time the outrageous humor of the situation could not longer be hidden and this performance ended, never to be used again. Despite all his overt attempts to make us angry, his boyish enthusiasm had won our hearts. He became a person and then we could relate to him.

In Searle's courageous paper, he presents evidence concerning *modes, motives* and the *patient-therapist relationship* related to "The Effort to Drive the Other Person Crazy." The previously mentioned occurrence could certainly be seen in this context, especially when the enormous effort on the part of the patient is considered. Another patient, who did not respond to our efforts, was even more steadily consistent. For a period of eight months he told me, in private as well as during group therapy hours, "There is nothing you can do to help me." I can still hear the cruel, bitterly sarcastic tone in which he repeated this statement literally hundreds of times. He was quite correct.

When either the prolonged silence, the withdrawal or the prolonged attack is no longer necessary for the patient, his group therapy behavior is not remarkably different from that seen in and reported from so many clinics treating the non-psychotic.

Differences, of course, there may well be and observers will no doubt clarify this issue as investigation proceeds. The great problem for both the therapist and his group, however, is the initial period of two to four months. It is during this time that the new patient tests out the resiliency of the group, its ability to tolerate his clearly and obviously aberrant behavior, before he ventures to the point of trusting the group to know something about his concerns. Having apparently concluded that some reliability and trust can exist in the group, he now proceeds to investigate the next important question, "How much?"

The following verbatim excerpt from such a session serves in part to illustrate this point. Most of the earlier psychotic material has subsided, a couple of members are still hallucinating but one would never suspect this from their group performances. We see how carefully and delicately these patients probe into their environment to see how it will react. The caution, the rather remarkable politeness which has settled over this previously quite recalcitrant group, and the tendency for one patient to act as major spokesman, despite the therapist's attempts to involve others, all can be seen in sharp focus.

T = Therapist
S, L, W, H, C, B, N = Patients

T: "You're depending upon how confident you feel at the time, to know if you can trust yourself to the meeting?"

S: "I'm not sure if you see how I think about it. Until just a couple of days ago, I felt that I didn't want to take part in these meetings and it seemed that the effect could be bad. I was doing well and wanted to leave well enough alone—but I haven't explained it very well. I don't want to have any interference that might cause some harm to me and that is what I thought would very likely come out of those silent meetings. Now although I still feel that I am making progress, I would like to take advantage of these meetings. I can't see any harm but I'm still afraid to introduce anything."

T: "What things could happen in our group here that could be harmful?"

S: "When I talk, everyone's attention is focused on me and my attention is focused on myself and I really don't trust myself well enough to like that. I *can* say just about anything and I don't know what I am going to say."

T: "You might expose some sore area perhaps?"

S: "Yes—or something about my personality that I would like to cover up."

T: "Have you any feeling like this, L?"

L: "It seems to me that I have said what I have to say before. I just can't say anything. I have to think what I want to say beforehand."

T: "You haven't felt that something might slip out?"

L: "No. I guess I'm kind of careful about what I bring out."

T: "You felt you had to be careful at times. Have you felt like this, W?"

W: "One day I feel this way, one day I don't."

T: "Do you feel you have to be careful?"

W: "Every once in awhile and it is sometimes a little frightening."

T: "How about you, H?"

H: "I used to feel that way. I think about all I am going to say. I have figured if I am going to get well I've got to speak out and get their reaction."

T: "You feel you have to check the group?"

H: "If all of them don't go along, you've got a chance to look it over and find out where you were wrong."

T: How about you, C?"

C: "A lot of the time I just think about what other people are saying. I don't think much about myself."

T: "Do you feel you ought to be careful?"

C: "Sometimes. Most of the time, I guess."

T: "Do you feel this way, B?"

B: "You have to be careful about your bad habits and everybody else. Just say what you want to say."

T: " 'Careful,' I suppose must have a lot of different meanings. In one way or another, S, your feelings are like a lot of other people's."

S: "I don't trust the group too well about things they may find out about me. While I like the group, I don't think it has the ability to understand me anyway, but I guess that is just skirting around the issue."

T: "Is it?"

S: "If I didn't value their feelings about me, they wouldn't be so important to me. While I have built up some friendships here, these depend upon my acting smooth and my seeming fairly fascinating in some ways. But there are some things in the past that I am sure would go over with a dull thud with the people here if they knew about them, so I guess I don't have confidence in the people all the way. . . ."

T: "Let's see if we can do something with this now. [Goes to blackboard behind him and writes the word 'careful'.] 'Careful' of what you say looks as if it had something to do with the relationship between you and the other members of the group. You feel a certain pressure as to whether they are going to approve what you say. What would happen if they didn't approve?"

Several patients: "They wouldn't listen."

S: "I wonder should I change or not. I tell myself that if they won't have me as I am, then they are not worthy of friendship. For years I have been wondering about how smooth I can be and how smooth I am."

T: "What do you think he means by 'smooth'?"

B: "Like you think smooth as a smooth person, a smooth talker...the way he carries on . . . well planned . . . he trusts everyone."

S: "That sounds about right. But it sounds emptier than I really thought it was. He is right. I guess it is pretty empty . . . ."

T: "You are developing something. What other things could happen in addition to their not listening?"

N: "First of all, you couldn't get a reaction. If the people didn't understand, they would lose interest and wouldn't react."

T: (More notes on blackboard.) "Wouldn't listen . . . wouldn't understand."

S: "I would like to bring up an example that I have wanted to bring up for a long time. It was about a year ago. I was looking through some of my sister's old mail that she kept. One of the girls she was writing to seemed to be classifying boys in two categories, those who were 'creeps" and those who weren't. I have always been afraid that I am going to be judged as a 'creep'—even by people who are the same thing.

N: "Being judged a 'creep' is up to the girl as an individual. To one girl you might seem like a 'creep' but to the other girl you might be very interesting. You have to judge what kind of girl it is. Rather than talk about yourself so much, try to find out something about her."

T: "You are suggesting that there might be more approval if you are interested in the other people in the group?

N: "I don't think you can put it as generally as that. An individual is an individual. You might talk about jazz to someone who isn't interested and she might consider you a 'creep' for it."

S: "There is a girl I know who, like me, is something of an outcast in our home town. She has gone to New York and is living there very fast and going around with a very 'arty' crowd . . . spending most of her time in Greenwich Village which is the place in New York where you want to go with these people who are pretty empty. She said that there are people she considers 'creeps' but some of them she feels are very nice people and she likes some of them very much. Now, this does not seem as wonderful as it first did when she first said it."

T: "This kind of evaluation may change? A 'creep' can meet with approval?"

S: "There is more to a person than one quality."

T: "Something to do with understanding?"

S: "And whether you want to understand and how much you want to judge people—although I don't like that word I have to use it."

T: "This is something C has been interested in all along, judging and being judged. It begins to look more and more that being careful is pretty well connected with the feeling of being judged. What do you think, L?"

L: "Being careful and judging everybody kind of goes together, I think."

T: "This comes up again and again, doesn't it? I wonder why it is so important. Each one of you people feel that the other is going to judge you."

(Clarifying discussion in which T apparently demonstrates that the group judges excessively and complains when *it* is judged.)

S: "I would say this group doesn't judge other people very much. Although still we have to act as if we thought that everyone was judging us. While B was talking I glanced around and I realized that there were only a couple of people here that I have made any real judgment about or tried to. So there won't be any mystery, I'll say who. W, because he seems so different and he is so hard to understand, and the other one is B himself, because I think he feels he is better than ordinary people and that is very exasperating to me. So, I am judging him all the time. I just can't take anybody splitting things on the basis that he . . . he seems to feel that he is on a higher plane . . . he gets this from his religion and that is something that I am usually furious about. I'm not sure whether I have any reason to be or not."

T: "Two people you have judged, one on the basis of difficulty understanding . . . ."

S: "I am so furious about why W is the kind of person he is."

T: ". . . and the other one on the basis of the feeling that you have that he feels he is better than other people. You say you don't understand that either."

S: "I hate it more than anything else. I don't know that I have tried to understand it. He seems to be telling everybody that everybody is wrong. That's no way to look at life."

T: "May I see if I can fit some of the pieces together? On the one hand you want understanding but you find you don't attempt to understand."

S: "I dislike it so much that I don't see any justification."

T: "Both of these judgements had to do with lack of understanding. Is it possible, gentlemen, that you judge when you don't understand? That you are troubled that you will be judged first, before you can be understood?"

It is, of course, quite obvious that "careful" or "caution" is the dominant theme. Therapist and patients seem to agree but on different levels of organization. The patients appear mostly concerned with differentiation at this point, while the therapist is struggling with integration.

ANALYSIS OF SESSIONS

As months turned into years, and patients came and departed, several factors concerning my group therapy with my schizophrenic patients were highlighted. I found, for example, that the sessions leaned heavily upon me. For a long time I aimed at the goal of group sessions in which the patients would "take over" and use me as their helper. I had the idea that they would benefit most from assumption of responsibility for their own therapy and a more classical image of the therapist as a "gently guiding" or navigating entity. Insofar as I can determine, this situation occurred so rarely as to be negligible in importance. They taught me a new image for a group therapist dealing with a schizophrenic population. By the simple process of not responding to any other method, they demonstrated that: If I took the responsibility for getting things started, bringing up matters which by being left unsaid were producing impasses, by actively and clearly demonstrating my engagement with the group, then and then only would they consistently respond. To use a somewhat limping analogy: If I pushed the group hard enough to get it rolling, it would roll with its own momentum for long periods. If, however, I did not push, it would simply wait immobile, until I did. As a group it seemed predominantly re-active, in contrast to the active forces which have appeared prominent in other groups with which I have dealt.

In order to gain more definitive information concerning the specific group behavior of these patients, a project was organized by Captain Leslie J. Shellhase, MSC. Specializing already in the study of group process, and having already observed patient-government activities for a considerable period, Captain Shellhase elected to use an already validated system, Bales Interaction Process Analysis. He trained as assistant, Mrs. Eve F. Dickman, and the two observers sat, watched and coded the sessions for a six-month period.

Shellhase reports as follows:

STUDY OF GROUP PROCESS IN GROUP PSYCHOTHERAPY*

The procedure of making direct observation of the schizophrenic subjects as they participated in group psychotherapy was initiated at what was the first group psychotherapy meeting for most of the subjects. Within the conference room earlier described, the two observers sat at a small table in a corner opposite the therapist. Behind the emergence of the observers into the periphery of the group therapy situation lay several months' training in the use of the observational instruments. Additionally, the armamentarium of the observers included an experience in which both the patients and the staff had become accustomed to the presence of the observers in other roles which were consistently extra-therapeutic. The senior observer had been the advisor to the patient-government, had been non-directive in this role. He had already established a situation in which the patient group and the staff group had to provide means of communicating with each other that did not depend upon his involvement. In a similar fashion, the patient group had found that the advisor's presence and interest did not relieve the group of the necessity to construct its own group organization and to develop its own modes of operation. The junior observer had functioned as ward secretary since the inception of the project. In this capacity, she likewise was present at, but not a part of, the therapeutic situation. She did not figure in the therapeutic process of correction of aberrant mentation and behavior.

At the outset, the therapist briefly explained the presence of the observers. He told of their interest in how the group solved its problems

---

* The research experience described here is elaborated in a doctoral dissertation, *The Group Life of the Schizophrenic Patient: A Social Work Investigation.* Washington, D. C., Catholic University of America Press, 1961.

and added that the observers would continue to be present during group psychotherapy. There was at no time an instance in which any of the participants in group psychotherapy, patient or staff, attempted to place the observers in a participant role. Rather, the observers were scarcely noticed during the group psychotherapy sessions. Even when a patient feared that he had said too much, he would discharge his concern about this toward a member of the treatment staff or toward another patient. If he should verbalize a concern that someone was noting what he had said and would attempt to harm him with these data, he did not direct this toward the observers, who at that very moment were busily engaged in taking accurate note of what he was saying. Rather, he would direct this toward the "real" people in his environment who were, in truth, issuing therapeutic challenges to his thoughts and actions.

It is not claimed that the observers achieved such anonymity that they were unnoticed. What was achieved was a working position which respected and was respected by the participants within the field of observation. The observers took the position that they had nothing to hide from the participants, but that the details of their work were rather complex and did not translate themselves immediately into anything very meaningful to the subjects. On the basis of being innocuously non-contributory, the observers were accepted by the subjects.

One instrument used in collecting the observational data was Bales' system of Interaction Process Analysis.[9] This system had the advantage that extensive observations of experimental problem-solving groups via the system had earlier been reported and thus a standardized description of "normal" group behavior was available. This system took account of a number of factors of group interaction which bore upon the behavior of individuals within such a group situation as group psychotherapy. It concerned itself with both the originator and object of interaction, with the two distinct functions of (1) problem-solving and (2) affective exchange. Through this means, the behavior of the group-as-a-whole could be viewed as well as the behavior of each individual member. In addition, a record of topical content was maintained. In this, an account was accumulated not only of the material discussed but also of additional impressions of the observers not totally described within the Interaction Process system.

Results

The behavior of the total group was at some variance with the behavior of the "normal" groups which had earlier been reported via this system. Particularly in the area of interaction which had to do with affective exchanges did the subject group show some constricture. The sort of affective exchange which carries the message, "I like you very much; I like your ideas and ways of operating; you can count on me to be your friend," was not one that was made with much facility by the schizophrenic subjects. With even less frequency and greater difficulty a subject would be able to reciprocate such a message. A group psychotherapy meeting is not a place where exchanges of superficial sentiment occur. Such a meeting is a serious occasion. It expects a serious commitment on the part of its participants. In that regard, it was with gravity that a subject would resist engagement in the therapeutic process as he saw that challenges were issued to his current modes of behavior. It was perhaps with even greater seriousness that a subject would move toward an engagement in the therapeutic process, wherein he would declare the relevancy of the treatment situation to his own condition.

Tensions can arise within individuals as a product of their group experience. Even the declaration of a firm feeling of positive association can generate tension or uneasiness. To a more marked degree, the expression or implication of hostile feelings can give rise to feelings of tension in both the individual who experiences the hostile feelings and those others who may be either the objects or the provokers of such feelings. Within human group experience, such discomfort is perceived in the self or in others as not contributing to the group goals or even allowing for the continuation of the solidarity of the group. Perhaps the most direct approach to such a condition, if not always the most effective, would be a "head-on" one in which the condition of tension would be made an object of specific group concern and efforts would be made to effect its resolution. A more frequent occurence, however, is the discharge of the tension by means of humor or some other type of "aside" which allows the individual or group, as the case may be, to secure relief from the built-up tension and to make a reorientation to the presenting task in a manner that is now free of the earlier tension.

What does occur, however, is an adjustment in the balance of the group which redirects the focus of group energies away from the situation of tension. The subjects of this study were unable to demonstrate mastery of this common means of dealing with the tensions that were generated. Because of the continued avoidance of tension-discharging behavior, the group appeared rather mirthless much of the time. Those occasions of high good humor among the group were exceedingly rare.

For some days, Patient B. had monopolized the group psychotherapy hour with an ongoing harangue against the therapist and the therapeutic process. This had begun to "wear" even on the most disengaged participant. On this occasion, he continued his soliloquy about the "persecution" to which he was subjected by the staff. "Oh they've got my head in a vise, held fast so I can't get away. And they keep tightening it. Every day, they give it two more turns counterclockwise." The therapist quietly commented that a counterclockwise turn would loosen a vise rather than tighten it. Patient B. was momentarily nonplussed and then commenced to laugh. He was joined by the entire group, patients and staff, in prolonged and robust laughter. The obvious error in Patient B.'s production had provided the occasion in which the group could indicate its evaluation of his use of the group's time. At the same time, it provided the occasion for Patient B. to make a change in direction without risk of losing the affections he had earlier gained.

The build-up of tension did not usually call forth an attempt at mastery, rather, an attitude of "dread" would appear from which the subjects made no effort to escape.

The experiencing of tension by the group tended to immobilize it into a silence which frequently became prolonged. These prolonged silences, upon occasion, had a flavor of resignation to a state of torpor within which each subject appeared to be more content to abide with his tensions. Through time, it became established that these silences were seldom terminated by a patient subject. Most frequently, they were terminated by the therapist speaking to the entire group so as to provide some direction. Even though the silence had been a "reprieve" from engagement in therapy, the response of the group usually indicated relief at being "delivered."

Within this situation, the function of the therapist as a leader and teacher of the subjects emerges in bold relief. The leadership of the group therapy endeavor remains the responsibility and personal charge of the therapist. The group of subjects is not self-sustaining in such endeavors. As an example of the role of the therapist, the phenomenon, earlier described, of the paucity of positive affective exchanges among the subjects may be examined for the responsiveness of the subjects to the activity of the therapist. The therapist must provide a model through his own behavior, in order that the subjects can learn to give expression to the stirrings of positive affect that are generated within the therapy situation. Clearly, the therapist provides leadership, in that he must first identify the occasions which call for expression of positive affect. He does this by means of his own utilization of such behavior toward the subjects.

It was noted that the subjects become able to reciprocate such feelings to the therapist. A subsequent development was that the subjects were enabled to make expressions of similar sentiment to each other. The development of *reciprocal* exchange of positive affect occurred among the subjects in a fashion that appeared related to the ultimate response of the individual subjects to the therapeutic experience. Those subjects whose ultimate response was one of success, i.e., those who upon discharge from the ward returned to duty and to a full responsibility for the ordering of their affairs, developed reciprocal positive affective exchanges with all other subjects who were successes. Additionally, they reciprocated such bids for similar relationship from those subjects whose ultimate response was one of failure. This latter condition was defined through a discharge from the ward to a situation less indicative of adequacy than return to duty, e.g., transfer to another ward for other types of treatment, separation from service for reasons associated with the current illness, transfer to an institution caring for chronic mental illness. These latter subjects, the failures, effected reciprocal positive affective exchanges *only* with subjects who were successes. Without exception, a failing subject who ventured such an affective exchange with a failing colleague did not secure reciprocation, and when he was the object of such a bid, he would not make response to it (Fig. 3)

Along a number of dimensions, individual patients became distinguished by their performance within group psychotherapy. Perhaps one of the most obvious demands that a group psychotherapy situation makes of its members is that they participate in verbal exchange. This demand is one which derives from the needs of the immediate situation, that communication within the therapeutic endeavor should be primarily verbal. Additionally, there is the more general demand that arises from the needs of the supporting society, that its members develop and utilize an ability to communicate with each other with some accuracy and effectiveness. As-

POSITIVE SOCIAL EMOTIONAL INTERACTION AMONG THE SUBJECTS IN GROUP PSYCHOTHERAPY

$S^{1,2,3}$ = SUCCESSFUL SUBJECTS
$F^{1,2,3,4}$ = FAILING SUBJECTS

A = RECIPROCATED POSITIVE INTERACTION
B = POSITIVE INTERACTION INITIATED WITHOUT RESPONSE
C = POSITIVE INTERACTION RECEIVED WITHOUT RESPONDING
D = MUTUAL AVOIDANCE OF POSITIVE INTERACTION

OBJECTS OF INTERACTION

		S^1	S^2	S^3	F^1	F^2	F^3	F^4
	S^1	–	A	A	D	A	D	A
	S^2	A	–	A	A	A	B	A
INITIATORS	S^3	A	A	–	A	A	A	C
OF	F^1	D	A	A	–	B	B	D
INTERACTION	F^2	A	A	A	C	–	B	D
	F^3	D	C	A	C	C	–	D
	F^4	A	A	B	D	D	D	–

Fig. 3

suredly, verbal communication is the major medium of exchange in group psychotherapy.

Analysis of the behavior of this group of schizophrenics in therapy revealed that the extent of participation of each individual was related to his ultimate response to therapy. When the subjects were ranked according to the extent of their verbal contribution, those subjects who ultimately returned to duty were found to be heavier contributors than any of the subjects whose ultimate response to therapy was one of failure, with a single exception. The exception was a subject who had, clinically, begun to show promise as a therapeutic candidate, when he "broke therapy" by failing to return from his Christmas holiday leave.

It would appear that if an individual participated verbally in the group situation in a fashion that was relatively extensive, this behavior was likely to be associated with his successful response. Upon occasion, participation of some subjects who ultimately failed approached the extent of participation of the successful subjects, but such production was not sustained. Additionally, there were qualitative differences in these two performances of which more will be said later.

The employment of Bales' system of group observation focuses upon two aspects of group behavior, the problem-solving process and the solidarity-achieving process. The problem-solving process in group psychotherapy with schizophrenic patients is complex. It requires that problems be identified and located. This is a procedure which requires extensive personal involvement because the problem is always found to be related to failure in living associated with the processes of schizophrenia and it is always located within the life experience of the individual participant. The schizophrenic appears ill-prepared to relate himself to others. The very defects to which he is expected, in group therapy, to address himself, are those which he has earlier used pathological means to deny, or to attempt to isolate. To be able, then, to participate appropriately in the therapeutic process requires of an individual that he accept the soundness of the therapeutic endeavor and the germaneness of this process to his own condition.

When the participants in this process were ranked by their contribution to the resolution of problems dealt with by the group, the major individual contributor was the therapist. This is accepted as being consistent with his role as leader of the group's endeavors. Among the subject-patients, there was a clear-cut division between the successful patients and the failing ones. *The contribution to the resolution of problems by the least active subject in the successful group was greater than that of the most active member of the failing group.* While the failing group in this study was numerically superior to the successful group, its total contribution

(17 percent) to the problem-solving was less than a third of that of the successful group (58 percent) and considerably less than the contribution by the therapist himself (24 percent).

Viewed as a total group and compared with the performance of "normal" groups in experimental situations, the effect of setting upon group behavior becomes somewhat clearer. It was noted that the group of schizophrenics in group therapy was consistently able to establish and maintain communication within itself at least as easily as the "normal" groups. It is considered that this occurred as a result of the therapeutic milieu. The milieu, particularly the personnel who staff it, took recognition of the past difficulties in communication that the schizophrenic subjects had had. At all times in this therapeutic experience, the staff endeavored to extend and improve the communicative abilities of the subjects. This had the effect of extending the work of establishing and maintaining communication far beyond the specific situation of group psychotherapy. Thus, within group psychotherapy, there was less need for attention to communication itself. Rather the energies of the group could be directed toward more advanced elements of the problem-solving process. The group was able to address itself to those aspects which bear more heavily upon the resolution of problems, such as sharing of evaluations or the venturing of suggestions.

In the area of the solidarity-achieving and maintaining of social-emotional interaction, two kinds of behavior were noted which were in direct opposition to each other. This opposition is so definite that the two orders of behavior are called "positive and negative social-emotional interaction." The positive interaction is that behavior which is calculated to bolster the *esprit* of the group and/or the morale of the individual by the expression of a sentiment which indicates a pledge of solidary feeling or willingness to affiliate with others within the group situation. Negative interaction, on the other hand, consists of behavior which attempts to effect or retain a lack of union with the group and its purposes. It may consist of a rather passive denial of any relevancy of the group to oneself or may range to an aggressive attempt to discredit the group or its members.

The behavior of the subjects indicated similarity of behavior in one type of relationship—that with the therapist. Without exception, the therapist established a reciprocal exchange of positive affect with each subject-patient. It would appear that within this relationship, each subject, despite his ultimate response to the therapeutic experience, was able to give of himself sufficiently to create this mutual sharing of positive sentiments. It was in exchanging positive affect with each other that the successful subjects became distinguished from the failing ones. *Without exception, each successful subject effected a reciprocal exchange of posi-*

tive affect with each other successful subject. In addition, they affected similar exchanges with some failing subjects, and attempted such exchanges with other failing subjects who did not reciprocate. In only one instance did a successful subject rebuff an offer of positive affect from a failing subject. *The failing group, in contrast, did not effect a single reciprocally positive affective exchange among its members.* Such exchanges were made only with a successful member or with the therapist. Even though most failing members made such an overture to some other failing member, on no occasion was it responded to in kind.

For other aspects of Shellhase's observations, see also references 120 and 121.

I also learned that the patients saw me as having a certain educational responsibility. Here again I was required to depart from my preconceived image. Gradually they succeeded in teaching me the real depth and breadth of their social inadequacies as a group. Apparently their schizophrenic way of life had so consistently and seriously interfered with their learning opportunities that many social techniques "taken for granted" in the normal person were simply absent in my schizophrenics; not denied, not repressed, not forgotten, not unconscious, simply not there.

Erikson and Marlowe touched on this point[5] but its far-reaching importance did not become clear to me until much later. They pointed out this aspect of the schizophrenic's task performance, whereas I became aware of it principally in the matter of general naivete, unsophistication. For example, several had no real working knowledge of politeness, forms of social address and manners, giving them the appearance of "yokels." One had to be taught to clean his fingernails, another how to eat a meal without spoiling the appetites of all around him. Approximately one-third had to be taught that other patients had names and appreciated the politeness of having them known and used. A similar percentage had to learn that braggadocio as a social form is less than useful.

Sullivan,[136] in discussing some of his experiences with milieu therapy, states, "The truly sympathetic person lives with the schizophrenic on a primary basis of assisting in the growth by experience of a body of *relatively undeveloped* tendencies to interpersonal relations; the situation is one of education broadly conceived, not by verbal teaching but by communal experience —good tutoring." The point I wish to make is that in the group therapy situation, all patients together, all staff nearby and the therapist at the head of the table, a subtle non-verbal educational process is taking place, in which patients are taught by example many of the aspects of successful group participation. It is a point that I cannot stress too heavily. Many times I have felt that those factors in my group therapy sessions most relevant to change in the patient were predominantly non-verbal.

Most important of all the things I learned was that group therapy can be undertaken successfully with acute schizophrenic patients. To be sure, it cannot be said to compare in liveliness and drama to a group of husbands and wives met in a therapeutic situation aimed at improvement in marital relationships, but it has its moments. It does require a certain doggedness and persistence and reliability on the part of the therapist probably somewhat in excess of that necessary in neurotic groups. It does require special techniques to ensure the attendance of certain members. It is a time-consuming and slow process, containing many a hiatus, many periods when the therapist is completely at sea, not really knowing what—if anything—is going on, but it can be useful.

In all fairness, I should mention that it does take a good deal out of the therapist. Prolonged attacks, persistent virulent hostility and defeatism do not provide for him the most pleasant of all possible environments. He must be able to withstand long periods of being alone and friendless, for one cannot come close to the schizophrenic patient without feeling the sting of his defensive attempts to drive the other person crazy. This is a "fact of life" when dealing with a schizophrenic population and will not disappear for being ignored. It must be considered and met.

THE EMERGENCY SESSION

Despite the staff's efforts to head them off,* altercations between patients occur from time to time. With the thesis that every occurrence is a legitimate opportunity for therapeutic investigation, I initiated the emergency group meeting. When an altercation takes place, the staff is instructed as follows: separate the combatants *but only far enough so that they can't strike each other,* and encourage them to argue about whatever it is. Conventionally, in contrast, the attendant is trained to separate the combatants by considerable distance, often taking one to another ward to "cool off." In doing this he does achieve quiet, of course, but loses whatever opportunity is present for the clarification of issues or distortions.

Secondly, he is instructed to notify the doctor, who sizes up the situation and, if indicated, calls an emergency group meeting, discontinuing other scheduled activities. The session is held in the customary group therapy setting, all factors being identical to a regular session excepting that of time.

The doctor opens the session with a brief statement like, "Something has gone into action here. Our job is to get it back into words." Then, turning to a responsive group member, he says, "Suppose you start. What did you see?" Haltingly at first, the story gradually comes out as one after another gives his version. In nearly all cases, the majority of group members are caught up in the emotional storm and are engaged in the immediacy and genuineness of the group problem.

Let me illustrate with such an event. The main characters were John Henry, Giuseppe and I.

John Henry was a big fellow, a strong paratrooper whose interest in legal matters, together with his passionately destructive attitude towards authority figures had led him into such an anxiety-provoking situation that he was left with no out but psychosis. His omnipotent and delusional phase was on the

---

* Because we knew that apologies would be necessary later and that they wouldn't help.

wane and two important things were occurring: one, he was exploring with me the relationship between himself and his father; and two, he had progressed to the point of taking and keeping an offward job as an animal caretaker in one of the laboratories in the research division.

His father was a stereotype of what is usually called the "four-flusher." He had built up a moderately substantial fortune as a salesman only to become destitute in his forties when his embezzlements were uncovered. Since that time, he had been consistently in and out of trouble, frequently calling upon his son (the patient) to bail him out, make good his bad checks, etc. It was becoming apparent that the patient always responded and did get some satisfaction out of the reversed dependency situation.

Giuseppe was an Italian boy as his name indicates and a real problem for both the patient John Henry and me. John Henry was the president of the patient-government group and Giuseppe was an obdurate obstructionist in the group's plans. For me, he was a problem because I could not establish a relationship with him or aid my staff in doing so. Giuseppe would talk about cameras, but nothing else.

John Henry had dropped into my office in the morning and somewhat casually inquired concerning my confidence in his ability to carry on his job. I had accepted his action as a bid for reassurance and assured him of my confidence.

In the gymnasium, John Henry played in the basketball game with unusual intensity, several times became angry at Giuseppe. As the group left the gym, Giuseppe said something to John Henry, whereupon, without warning, John Henry suddenly picked him up, strode over to a balustrade and held Giuseppe over it by his ankles—a potential drop of thirty feet—head down. The accompanying technicians were frozen with surprise, fortunately elected to remain frozen and after some seconds that seemed like hours, John Henry shook his head and drew Giuseppe back over the balustrade to safety.

At the group meeting which followed, there was a consider-able show of feeling against the victim, one rather callous member suggesting that he should have been dropped. Giuseppe admitted that he had been frightened and in so doing expressed himself in a most insipid, giggling, childlike fashion—giving us a clue as to why he would not risk relating. John Henry could not seem to explain himself other than to say "something inside me kept building and he just set it off."

I pressed him concerning what had kept building and the story finally came out. He had become increasingly anxious in his job, bothered continually with fantasies about letting all the animals loose. He had wanted to let me know this in the morning and I hadn't responded to his cue. He had kept on with the job because he wanted my work to go on successfully and he didn't want to be the first patient to fail me and thus hurt my reputation.

"Oh," I said, "You've been trying to win medals for me."

"Well, of course," he responded, as if surprised that I hadn't known.

"Then I've placed you in exactly the same position your father always does."

"Uh, huh," followed by a sigh of relief in which patient and therapist joined. The tension was lifted, the problem resolved and the therapist went back to work wondering, "Will I ever learn?"

Chapter 3

EXPERIENCES WITH PATIENT GOVERNMENT

Patient government in action is described with illustrative examples, demonstrating its areas of significance in a therapeutic milieu, its limitations and some of the unique problems it poses for its patient members.

THE WORLD OF THE PATIENT in a closed mental hospital is indeed a special and unique one, rarely seen with much clarity by the staff, all too busy in its own. Fortunately for us all, sociologists have been given increasing opportunities to explore it during recent years (Caudill,[27] Stanton and Schwartz,[132] Goffman[52]) and we are somewhat less ignorant concerning its complexities as a result of their efforts. Let us consider the model proposed by Goffman, in which "two different social and cultural worlds develop, tending to jog along beside each other, with points of official contact, but little mutual penetration."[52]

It is possible to assume that one of the essential goals of a therapeutic milieu is to increase the degree of mutual penetration concerning these two worlds. Several pioneer investigators interested in the therapeutic community during recent years, Jones and Sivadon for example, have provided opportunities for patients to participate to some degree in decision making relevant to their institutional living.

Consequently, this factor, a patient advisory committee, was built into our design. It has become known as "patient-government" throughout the unit.

An organization of patients, so labeled, carries with it certain built-in hazards. For one thing, as Goffman points out, there is a potential for considerable "ceremonial ritual" or in more expressive language, "phoniness." Goffman[52, p. 80] says:

"In all instances of unified ceremonial life that I have mentioned, staff is likely to play more than a supervisory role. Often a high-ranking officer attends as a symbol of management and (it is hoped) of the whole estab-

47

lishment. He dresses well, is moved by the occasion, and gives smiles, speeches and handshakes. . . . When acting in this capacity, his interaction with inmates will take a special benign form; inmates are likely to show embarrassment and respect, and he is likely to display an avuncular interest in them. In the case of our very large and benevolently oriented mental hospitals, executive officers may be required to spend a goodly portion of their time putting in an appearance at these ceremonial occasions, providing us with some of the last places in modern society in which to observe a lord-of-the-manor feudal role."

Indeed, if a "patient government" has neither responsibility nor authority and furthermore cannot be provided any because of the restrictions placed upon the staff by the community, then we should indeed be wary of introducing another pretense into lives already so seriously troubled by inner pretensions.

The fact, however, that our patients were all soldiers, still "in the Army" and being paid regularly, became most useful at this juncture. The soldier, the world over, does have responsibility for his own housekeeping, whether he be in a barracks or a tent. He does have the responsibility of planning his leisure time and, most important of all, he does have the responsibility of learning the "semantics of soldiering," of which more later. With this group of patients, then, it was legitimate and reasonable that since they continued to receive pay as soldiers, they should continue to "earn their pay" as other soldiers wherever possible. Therefore, when their patient government group was formed, the responsibility for the housekeeping on the ward was turned over to it. For three and one-half years, the daily work has been parceled out, made into a "detail roster" in typical Army fashion, kept posted on the bulletin board and enforced by the patients.

Planning for the effective use of his leisure time is another responsibility of the active soldier which could be emphasized in this context. When satisfactorily organized, group theatre parties, picnics, sightseeing tours, fishing trips and the like, were all possible. The achievement of planning and successfully undertaking ventures into the "outside world" as a group became so important as to eventually constitute the central theme of a majority of the meetings. "Getting away from the hospital for awhile" seemed to be one objective upon which there could be high consensus on the part of the patients. The staff insisted this be done as a group and in such a manner as to have each member answerable to the group for his conduct. Thus, another wide area of patient behavior was made available for inspection by all concerned.

GENERAL MEANING FOR STAFF

By far the most important function of the patient government group, and indeed the only one which consistently persuades the staff of its value, is its potential for the members to learn methods of group behavior which lead to more successful outcomes. For example, in routine dealing with superiors or authoritative persons, it is important that one's requests be presented in such a fashion that the authority-figure will be allowed to approve them.* Simply, the request should be so designed that the answer will come back, "Yes. Go ahead." The ordinary citizen gradually acquires this skill as he learns the innumerable subtle maneuvers necessary for the comfortable achievement of a reasonable number of "successes," e.g., he learns how to plan the request for his vacation in such a way as to have it approved for the time most nearly suiting his own convenience.

In contrast, our investigations demonstrate a remarkably consistent failure potential in the schizophrenic population we have been allowed to study. So striking is this finding that a concept of "ingenious failure" has been developed by members of the field investigating teams, especially those who interviewed the work group (office force, Army squad, cadre) from which the

---

* Let me hasten to reassure the sophisticated reader that no patient is taught that authority is necessarily "correct" or charismatic. Many a schizophrenic, especially the paranoid, appears to have attitudes towards authority that are far from unrealistic — his problem in living, however, is compounded by his being cynical rather than skeptical or as Sullivan put it, mistaking stupidity for malice.

patient was hospitalized. It has appeared at times that the group behavior of the schizophrenic becomes so failure-oriented, so precise in "oppositeness" from that of his fellows, as to allow for the possibility of its being "planned," "designed" or "programmed" for just such a consequence.

An example of this curious behavior might be enlightening. A group of the ward patients were working out a plan for "off-ward passes" or ground privileges. Their meeting was being monitored by the group process investigator, Captain Leslie J. Shellhase, MSC, who reports that they did indeed discuss the logical parameters of the situation, such as available hours, conflicts with scheduled activities, attitude of the doctor in charge, etc. However, despite clear evidence of their ability to properly evaluate the situation, they proceeded, just before the meeting ended, to "junk" all this information and made a large general request for passes of such magnitude as to be ridiculous in terms of what was possible, and, of course, to force a refusal. In this case, their proposal was returned to them for further consideration.

In discussing this behavior, we considered the possibility that it was designed to obtain further information, such as a reply, "You can't have this, but I'll tell you what you can have," in some ways similar to the classical bargaining maneuver in which both parties to a transaction engage in an elaborate ritual ostensibly aimed at establishing the price, e.g., the buyer offering half of what he expects to pay, and the seller demanding twice what he expects to receive, as the opening gambit.

However, clear information was readily available to the effect that the ward doctor, not a "bargainer," did not engage in these tactics. It is possible that as a group they did not believe this to be the case and explored a further testing maneuver. However, taken out of context and isolated as a specific piece of group behavior, it did appear "crazy, asking for the moon," and was quite consistent with the type of behavior which had been reported to us by the persons who had worked with them as individuals prior to hospitalization.

As part of a more rigorous study of the self-governing activities of these patients as a group, Captain Shellhase[120] reports that the vast majority of the group's plans were made only in skeletal form, taken to the staff "for approval"; as a part of which process "they would then succeed in getting the staff to fill in the details of these plans." Statistically analyzing the material, he points out that during the observation period:

92 plans were proposed
66 plans were carried to completion
    60 depended upon staff (as above)
     6 were independently successful

In possession, now, of these more objective data, we may return to the example and note the possibility that the schizophrenic group decided at the last minute to hand the problem over to me, obviously all jumbled up, like a child who hopefully hands a broken toy to the parent with the magical expectation, "Fix it, Daddy."

By this time it must be obvious that whatever analogies we propose in order to amplify or illustrate, the general problem is the same: Smooth, "adult" or "mature" group functioning is not customarily seen in these patients even in a protected environment. Consequently, it was important that we provide an opportunity where even 10 percent of their plans (the six independent successes) could come to an adult conclusion, and they receive the feedback in mastery-satisfaction which is probably the *only* real gratification for anyone's being an adult. To wit: without the group government, not even these six group successes would have occurred.

Let me try to amplify and (hopefully) clarify my point here concerning the potential value of group government for a population of young schizophrenic males. First, let us assume that social hierarchy, together with levels of authority, is a fact of life, a reality as it were. Further, let us accept that knowledge concerning social structure—what one may do or may not do in a given situation at a given time—is one of the necessary requirements for comfortable living. If we now apply this measure to the schizophrenic soldiers we have studied, we find them to be startlingly deviant. For example, the ordinary soldier quickly learns that there are many different ways of standing at attention and that one varies these depending upon the situation, who is watching, the type of military formation, the "tastes" of the sergeant, etc.—the semantics of soldiering. In contrast, the schizophrenic soldier defines "attention" in his own manner, without evident regard for the social climate. If he defines being at attention as "rigid-ramrod," then this is the only kind of attention there is and he persists in using it, whatever the occasion. It is of interest, in passing, that both Kraepelin and Bleuler did describe him as "rigid."

Now, my argument continues, he must learn to deal with society and its authorities in terms relevant to the manner in which they define the situation, *in addition* to the way that he does. Consequently the patient-government group can be set up in such a way that it has increasing independence and success *depending upon the degree to which it also considers the needs of authority-persons.* As ward-officer, I could act—or delegate the nurse to act—as "approving authority." We tried to maintain in this role the image of average responsible authority. That is: We basically wished to approve, *but* our approval was contingent upon the government group's knowing enough about our problems as to present their requests in such a manner as to allow us to approve.

To wit: They wanted off-ward privileges. I wanted them to have off-ward privileges. What were the factors to be considered relevant? What did they know about the attitude of the Chief of the Department of Neuropsychiatry, of the Hospital Commander, of the prevailing climate in Washington concerning the treatment of mentally ill persons, of the local newspaper treatment of soldiers who behaved in aberrant fashions? Simply: How much were they aware that I, the socially designated approving authority, had to consider many aspects of the situation in addition to the basic request?

Frequently, they demonstrated considerable awareness of such problems. Quite as often, however, some relevant factor was completely overlooked or ignored. When this was pursued, the question might be, "How can we find out?" The answer, "You could ask," at times appeared to strike them as a sudden shock. For some reason, it seemed characteristic of the subjects of this study that they portray themselves as "innocent." An illustrative story, coming from a different surrounding, may help to further clarify. Military psychiatrists at basic training centers, where the "raw recruit" receives his first eight weeks of training, report this typical experience again and again (both with soldiers who are later designated "schizophrenic" and those who are not): A young soldier, having difficulty, is referred for psychiatric consultation to the Mental Hygiene Consultation Service (the Army's community clinic). He is telling about his self-evaluation as a failure, "I can't do twenty push-ups. I can barely make it to twelve." He is then asked, "How many are the others doing?" at which point he looks at his questioner in amazement—suddenly realizing that he not only doesn't know, but hasn't looked.

To return to this factor with the ward patients, where it stands out as a group problem in distinction to the individual one noted above, the typical experience would be structured something like this: The president of the patient government group would be talking to the ward nurse and would say, "We've decided to go to the National Theater next Thursday and see the play."

"All right," replies the nurse. "How will you get there?"

"Well," replies the patient delegate, beginning to show discomfort, "We thought that you . . ."

"Maybe I can help," says the nurse. "How will you get the tickets and how much do you want to pay?"

At this point, the patient delegate shows surprise as he replies, "Never thought of that . . ."

Hopefully, it will be obvious by now that the "authority role" of the ward group—in relationship to the patient government function—was markedly different from the general ward milieu of helpfulness, interest and curiosity. Admittedly, as a psychiatric treatment group we did not play the authoritarian role well or with the conviction of field Army people, but we essayed it in this fashion as best we might. Sometimes too, it was amusing to both patients and ourselves when our "authority role playing" was less than convincing. However, we were usually forgiven, in terms of our earnest endeavors to get the point across.

Admittedly, the simpler solution would have been to provide a separate administrative staff or person, as in the Chestnut Lodge arrangement reported by Stanton and Schwartz.[132] With this maneuver, the robes of the authoritarian role would not have had to be handed around from one person to another in the staff. However, this was not practical in our setting and indeed its absence called upon the staff for greater flexibility, probably a benefit in and of itself.

POTENTIAL VALUE FOR INDIVIDUAL PATIENTS

Patients customarily elected their own officers, usually selecting a president and secretary, at times adding a vice president. Balloting was open or secret, depending upon attitudes existent at the time. The only specific instructions regarding meetings were that they should be scheduled regularly—various groups decided upon one to three meetings per week—and that the advisor, a social group worker, would meet with them. Liaison with the ward officer and nurse was maintained through their elected leaders.

In general, it was found that a patient who was elected president would later have a successful outcome to his treatment and return to military duty. In the president role, such a patient would have the primary duty of organizing and conducting the meetings. For many, it appeared to be the first such opportunity in their lives. The job was approached seriously and with every evidence of genuine commitment, whether in positive or negative terms (discussed later).

The observer noted continually that the president acted in the interests of law and order, as it were. Representative of the group's wishes in this regard, he acted in his official capacity to enforce the group's own ethical standards. One of these unwritten laws apparently went something like this: "Leave symptoms outside of these meetings." The patient group is here being entirely consistent, for quite early in this study it became apparent that symptoms were primarily for use as communication with the staff, wherein the real fate-determining power lay. In marked contrast, within a group of patients dealing with patients concerning the interests of patients, symptoms were taboo.

A recent example illustrates the precision of the patients' distinction: A patient who had been fending off the staff by shouting, "Listen at me," repetitively at a rate of twenty to fifty times per minute for a period so prolonged that two nearby wards were complaining, was escorted to a patient government meeting by two technicians. They succeeded in extricating themselves from his grip to get him into the door of the meeting room. As he passed through the door, he stopped the shouting. He participated throughout the business session with the others for forty-five minutes, and only with the disbanding of the meeting and his emergence again through the door into the sight of the technicians, did he begin shouting again.

In the rare instance that a patient would violate this code and present a symptomatic facet of himself to the group, they would immediately react to "straighten him out," usually through the leader whose actions they would clearly support.

Shellhase's notes concerning such an episode demonstrate both the general trend of a meeting and the group's response to an individual member's symptomatic presentation of himself:

There was no meeting of the group on 11 December 19—, the regularly scheduled time. On this date, G. (the president) came to the worker and asked if he would be available for the meeting during the noon hour. There was no mention made of the failure to have a meeting on the preceding day.

As soon as the meeting was convened, G. asked the members if they wanted to make plans for the weekend. O. then proposed that the group make a trip downtown. Immediately in response to this, E. raised many questions regarding organization of the trip. For example, he asked how the group would get there, how many would go, whether the car would have a heater, etc. It was noted that G. and O. supplied the answers to E.'s questions. After solicitation of the members, it was developed that only E., O. and G. were interested in going. At that point, O. suggested that they should drop this proposal. G. immediately concurred. It was noted that O. had made his suggestion of dropping the plans in a hesitant way, and that his reaction to G.'s immediate concurrence in this was one of hurt.

G. suggested that the group consider which post movies they would like to attend the following week. None of the members moved immediately on this. Customarily, J. has come up with ready suggestions. On this occasion, he asked for additional information as to the movies available. E. entered the discussion to ask more questions of an organizational nature as to the mechanics of their going to post movies. As the group continued to deliberate, G. suggested that they not plan to go to the movies, and instead stay on the ward nights working on the decorations for the Christmas party the following week. In response to this, E. suggested that afternoons would be better for the group to work than evenings because B. and O. were with their wives at night. This suggestion was incorporated into the plan by G. G. then began to seek the concurrence of each individual in the group.

While he was doing this, K. broke in with talk of his Company Commander. He spoke rather erratically about his concerns of what had happened prior to his hospitalization. G. dealt sympathetically with this, but after having heard him out, firmly suggested that K. save this for the group psychotherapy meetings.

G. then adjured all the members to get busy on the Christmas decorations. He mentioned, "The chairman [E.] has agreed to help with the fireplace." (In the previous meeting, with the assigning of duties to each member of the group, E. as chairman of the decoration committee, kept himself free of specific assignment.)

Before there was any response to G.'s remark, K. again entered the conversation with illogical talk. He expounded in considerable detail. During the time that he was doing this, it was noted that J., sitting directly behind K., began to grin broadly. O. also appeared uncomfortable and grinned some. During all this, G. again listened sympathetically and at the end of this said, kindly, "K., bring this up at next Monday's group therapy meeting." At that, G. adjourned the meeting.

The president customarily illustrated concern about the conduct of his group and, by his intensity, also demonstrated his enthusiasm for his own role. Furthermore, it was part of his job to present the group's wishes, findings and decisions to the staff. At times, he would do this alone, but usually would ask his group secretary to accompany him.

This probably provided him with his most difficult assignment. If he became able to satisfactorily represent his group to the staff and again satisfactorily report back to his own group concerning the staff's attitude, it would be virtually certain that his prognosis for return to duty was excellent. Indeed, in this aspect of his role, he was obliged to make some degree of bridge between the patient and the staff world and hopefully, of course, provide more than a mere bridge, even at times an opportunity for interpenetration of the two worlds.

In surveying those aspects of the milieu which may be significant, I believe the above point should be considered seriously. If a given patient can have the opportunity to find himself the single carrier of distortions from both groups, one to the other and back, if he can see and hear and feel the problems of distortion at first hand, it seems to me that his position is improved relative to the further understanding of his own distorting tendencies. In a way, his position is not unlike that of the psychiatrist portrayed by Ruesch and Bateson[109] as the bridging individual sufficiently sick to understand the sick world and sufficiently well to understand the healthy one.

VALUE FOR PATIENTS AS A GROUP

This study has demonstrated a factor which has intriguing possibilities: It would appear that if the outcome of the interaction between the "treater" and the "treated" is increased social success upon the part of the "treated," the interaction itself will be labeled "therapy."

Reflection upon this factor allows for certain conjectures. For example: Is "mental health" the possession and utilization of sufficient skills to insure a reasonably continuous line of successes in living? Conversely, is "mental illness" the absence of such skills, leading to the consequences of punishing rejection, failure and defeat, eventually hopelessness?

If we further sharpen the concept "successes in living" to require that it describe those social interactions which are assessed as gainful or profitable by both parties to a transaction, do we then discover in our grasp that essential ingredient of self-realization (otherwise known as self-confidence, ego strength, ego integrity), *which is necessary for the accomplishment of the next success?* And, that failures are sufficiently disorganizing to the self-image to militate against subsequent successes? Concluding, in a tremendous over-simplification, that "nothing succeeds like success" and by that token the therapist's aim should be the establishment of acculturative success for his patients?

Now to return to the specific application. For the schizophrenic in particular, the simple acquisition of group membership is an enormous hurdle, since any group demands interaction in mutually-agreed-upon terms as the price of membership. Consequently, it may well be that any grouping on the part of schizophrenic patients has a potentially therapeutic value, and we have not got the "sociatric plow ahead of the psychiatric oxen" as one of Sivadon's critics[123] has suggested. We might then anticipate a general reaction in the direction of health from any investment in the patient-government group. There did appear to be definite fringe benefits from time to time.

For example, a successfully planned, managed and executed fishing trip, lasting all day and culminating in such an excellent catch that the group was able to offer fish to the various staff members—much as the successful fisherman elsewhere offers them to his neighbors—did provide for a substantial increase in general group warmth and ease for a prolonged period.

Furthermore, group adventures of this type do also provide the opportunity for adventitious benefits. On one trip to the beach, the entire busload was refused admission to a beach because the group contained Negro members. Patients and staff alike reacted with indignation and returned welded into a more "solid" group. They had located a common enemy.

The following excerpt from Shellhase's notes illustrates the conduct of the group in what might be termed an "average" or "typical" meeting. As will be noted, the meeting proceeds somewhat informally, but hews to a general structure, perhaps not too different from a meeting of the grounds committee at the local country club.

Announcing the meeting to be open, R. stated that he wanted to resign his position as president. S. asked why he should want to do this. R. explained that he would be leaving the group shortly, and wanted to resign for that reason. There was no further response to this, nor was there any formal action taken regarding his resignation.

After a brief silence, S. asked what other business there was for the group to take up. R. suggested that they were entitled to one more post movie for the week. There was no further move toward acting upon this for several minutes at which time M. announced that he would get the movie schedule for the week following. R. was able to recall the movie schedule for the present week. M. selected the movie for Friday night. S. immediately said that the group should go to the movie on Saturday night. In the ensuing discussion, it developed that S.'s objections to the Friday night movie were that he had already seen it. At that point, T. entered the room. S. immediately asked T. what his position was regarding the movie. T., initially, was very cautious and asked a number of questions regarding who favored which movies. Ultimately, however, he cast his lot with M. S. then said that the group must wait for L. T. immediately bristled and asked, "Why?" S.'s response was, "He is part of this group." T. made some unintelligible noises, as if he felt that this were a new procedure in the group, but did not say anything.

Specifically resolving the issue regarding the post movie, S. went on to propose that the group should plan to go to the movie, *The Big Country,* on Sunday. S. then solicited the other members of the group for their support of this plan. R. declared that he would be absent on pass at that time. M. said that he was in favor of it. T. responded that he would not go because of the money involved, but that he favored the plan for the group. S. then declared that this group was a majority and then declared that this plan was adopted.

S. then wondered out loud about other plans that the group might make. Initially, he suggested that the group might wait until the next meeting to decide. After R. had reminded the group that the following

Monday was a holiday, Labor Day, S. agreed that there was a necessity for the group to make further plans at this time. R. then made several suggestions, a band concert, a trip to the river. S. verbally rejected these plans and went on to propose that the group should plan to go bowling, soliciting the others for support. T. gave him immediate and enthusiastic support to this as did M. R. quietly commented that he wasn't much in favor of this plan, but made no effort to dissuade the others from this decision.

The group then deliberated as to selection of post movies to be attended the following week. This discussion was led by S. It was observed that there was less effort on his part to "lead" the group in the direction of a decision than there had been earlier.

R. summarized the meeting, and then suggested that the group had one more item of business, that they needed to elect his replacement as president. M. immediately suggested S. as the replacement. R. then solicited the others who immediately agreed to S. for this office. S. easily accepted, making only a very mild protest.

S. then stated that there was one other item of business for the group, that they needed also to elect a new secretary. R. protested that B. was still secretary of the group and suggested that they should wait until his return from leave. S. then stated that B. had told him prior to going on leave that he wished to be replaced and R. immediately acquiesced. S. then asked the group for ideas regarding the position of secretary. T. proposed L. S. immediately turned this down, saying, "He is not interested." T. then proposed J. This produced a somewhat startled reaction on the part of the other members and T. was somewhat sheepish, saying, "Well, he's a member of the group."

At this point L. came into the room. S. mentioned that the group had been considering him as secretary. He asked L. if he would take the secretary's position. L. hesitated very briefly and then stated that he would accept this position. R. then quickly polled the other members and found that they were in favor of this.

S. then began to instruct L. in his job. He indicated that his duties would include making up the detail roster, and developing all the ideas for the group. In short, he defined L.'s duties as including all the work connected with either the office of president or secretary.

S. then started to review for L. the plans the group had made. He had scarcely begun this when R. interrupted to say that he felt that he could probably do this better since he had been taking notes on the meeting. R. then proceeded to review the plans in a very concise fashion.

Following this, S. suggested that if there was nothing further for the group to take up, it should adjourn. This was seconded by T., and the meeting was over.

INTRA-GROUP STRUGGLES

Contrastingly on two occasions, patients who did not eventually respond to treatment were elected president. In both instances, the strong tendency towards order suffered, not only in the conduct of the meetings, but in the area of communication back and forth with the staff. At times, patients attempted to correct this fault, but it was apparently very difficult for them to express dissatisfaction with their own leaders.

In one such meeting, Shellhase's notes report:

At 1200 hours, the patients returned to the ward from the mess hall. Immediately, H. went to an appointment with the therapist. The worker went to B. (the president), who asked if the worker wanted to hold the meeting now. The worker returned this question to B. B.'s response was to rise and walk with the worker to the conference room. They were followed shortly by J. As they were seated, K. entered carrying with him his correspondence file. He showed the worker the new shoes which he had purchased and told of buying a rain coat also, on this, his birthday. Following this, L. entered with a magazine, seated himself and began to read. M. entered carrying a book. He also seated himself in a far corner and began to read. After several minute's silence, B. began to glare at L. and finally said, "We're waiting on you, Bill." L. looked up from his magazine briefly, but did not respond.

M. then entered into a conversation with J. regarding plans for a trip. M. said to B., "J. makes the motion, I second it for a trip to Mount Vernon." B.'s response was to ask J. for confirmation of this motion. Having received it, he called for a vote. There was a favorable vote passed by B. himself, M. and J. Without any effort to draw L. or K. into the decision, B. declared the motion passed. M. then suggested that the group make plans for the time to go. J. suggested that the group leave the ward at 12:00 and return at 5:00 rather than the usual 10:00 to 3:00. M. countered this by explaining that it was necessary for the technicians to be back by 3:00. J. continued to press for later hours, saying that it would make for greater variety. B. then called for a pencil from the worker and some paper which was supplied by K. He began to write down the plans and dictated to himself, "time of departure 10:15." He did this without any acknowledgment of J.'s efforts to the contrary. It was noticed that J. appeared irritated and silent in response to this.

Immediately following this, K. was attacked by B. for his lack of attention to the group's plans. In response, K. insisted that he was attentive. "I have no damn desire to see another colonial mansion. I made a motion to go to a whorehouse, I'm still waiting for a second." In response to this rather heated expression, J. began talking, as if to himself, the only intelligible part caught by the worker was, "This would make psychiatric history." At that point, K. returned to working on his correspondence files.

B. then asked if there were any further plans. The question was brought up at that point by J. as to just when the group could make the trip. He asked the worker regarding this. The worker's response was that the best information could be provided by B., who was dealing with the situation while the worker was more familiar with the history of the numerous changes in the plans. In response to the worker's referring this matter to B., he made no response whatsoever. Rather, he responded, "Now we have to plan the movies." He then passed the movie schedule to J. who selected *Bell, Book and Candle,* suggesting that the group see this on Friday. There was no immediate action on this. As B. began to fumble, as if to act on this, the worker pointed out that the Friday movie was at Forest Glen. Immediately, M. said that a trip to Forest Glen was out. They then sat in an impasse. As J. began gently to push for action on his suggested movie, B. said, "We saw *Bell, Book and Candle* already. Also, the Friday movie. That leaves *First Man into Space.*" B. refused totally to accept and incorporate the suggestion made by J. J. did not elect to challenge B. when he said that these movies had already been seen, despite the fact that this was an impossibility. B. then pronounced that the group would see the movie on Saturday night. With that, he arose and left the room. J. looked helplessly toward the worker for several minutes. He then turned and began to berate K. for his lack of attention to the group and its deliberations. The worker received the impression at that time, as J. looked back to him, that he would have needed only to nod his head in agreement with J. and J. would have physically assaulted K. Instead, the worker turned and left the room.

Summary: It should be commented that prior to the time of this meeting, B. had been known to be increasingly upset. Several observers reported his responding as if to hallucinations earlier in this day.

Particularly what should be noted is the fact that on this occasion, B. utilized his symptoms in such a fashion as to spread confusion within the group and, as an end to this, to be able to enforce his own decisions upon the group members. This represents an unprecedented use of symptomatology by a leader of the group. It is difficult to predict the extent to which this will be tolerated by group members. Touching on this is the observation that as J. became increasingly frustrated in his efforts to deal rationally with B., it was not B., but rather K. who felt the force of his wrath, or would have with only slight additional provocation. It is further to be noted that as B. resorted to increasingly pathological behavior in the group, there was no effort by anyone excepting J. to engage him. It was at this point that M. withdrew totally from participation in the group deliberations."

Another example of patient's attempts to compromise between loyalty to their leader and the chaos which his ineffectiveness produced is provided by the following report. In this report, furnished by Lt. Col. Ralph W. Morgan, MSC, who succeeded Captain Shellhase and has continued the observations, the observer tries to aid in straightening out a chaotic situation with the ensuing result:

Worker asked R. (the president) if he wished to call the meeting to order, but he indicated that meetings "are usually held on Thursday." Worker then announced to the group that he had called a meeting as advisor to the group to give them the information that no arrangements had been made for the party on Thursday at Sgt. U.'s house since their president had not made the arrangements with the nurse. R. stated that "I wish to legally deny this," and questioned the advisor about this information. Worker stated that he had endeavored to have the president call a meeting of the group or appoint a committee to see about the arrangements, but that the president had not felt like doing either of these things. The worker stated further that he had no desire to tell the group what course of action to take, but that as he saw it, the group had a choice of several courses of action. The first of these courses of action would be to elect a temporary chairman to serve during the incapacity of the president. The worker did not get an opportunity to proceed further. R. ruled the worker "out of order." Worker pointed out that as president, R. had not as yet called the meeting to order. At this point R. called the meeting to order. U. was on his feet with eyes blazing asking for the floor. When recognized by the president, U. launched into a speech somewhat to the following effect:

"This patient government rests on the principles of democracy which are the same as those of the constitution and of this nation. I have risked my life for these principles, just as Lt. Col. Morgan has as I see by his ribbons, even though I have not served outside the country. The important thing is that we have a group which operates on a constitution and which cannot be coerced into doing anything contrary to these principles. We have elected officers and they are doing a fine job and we should support them down the line in spite of all attempts to coerce them from any source whatsoever."

Worker asked for the floor from the president and received permission to speak. Worker said that he believed that U. was referring to him when he said that the group should resist coercion, and he wanted to make clear that he was not there to tell the group what course of action to take. Anything they chose to do as a group was between them and the staff. The worker, as advisor, did feel that it was his responsibility to give them information upon which to make their decisions. The information he had to give them now was that nothing had been done to arrange for the party for which the group had voted. R. again denied that nothing had been done and asked where I got this information. Worker stated he knew from the nurse that there had been no official arrangements. R. then asked, "Can we call the nurse in here and see about that?" Worker said that representatives of the group could talk with the nurse after the meeting, but that he wished to set forth what he saw as possibilities for the group in getting this party planned. Worker then enumerated the choices before the group:

a. Elect a temporary chairman to serve during the incapacity of the president.
b. Vote to have a secretary assume the office of president.
c. Elect a new slate of officers.
d. Do nothing about this and let the party not come off.

Worker again stated that what was done was up to the group and that he was just the advisor.

R. said, "Yes, you are the advisor and I am the President, and I ruled very wisely in this matter."

V. sought recognition at this point and stated somewhat as follows:

"We all know that we sometimes forget things by just putting them off, things that really need to be done. We are very proud of our officers and they are doing a fine job, and we all support them. We thank you [nodding at the worker] for the information you have given us and we feel that this has cleared up quite a few things."

Worker agreed that this all had helped the group and the worker to understand much better how everything stood.

V. then proposed that Sgt. U. and Mrs. U. be appointed chairmen of a committee to arrange the party since it would be at their house. R., in a resurgence of his delaying tactics, asked V. to rephrase this and put it in the form of a nomination. V. did this, but before it could be seconded, Sgt. U. asked for and received the floor and gave his second long speech of the day. In effect, he said:

"I want to explain the purpose of this party. When I was on the ward upstairs, I was pretty sick and I am just now getting straightened around. I am lucky to have a good wife to talk to away from this place and I think everyone needs something like this. Some of you fellows have not been home or had any home cooking for a long time and I want you to have what I have.

"I want to say that I have been planning with the nurse for this party since it was going to be at my house, and we had to know what to buy and who was coming. I know that I was doing this informally, but I thought that everyone knew about this and that this was all right.

"I wish to turn down any idea that I be appointed a chairman. I think that working here together, we can decide everything that needs to be decided and work out the details with the nurse later."

R. then informed V. that "this overrules your nomination." At about this time, T. surprisingly came up with "a point of order." Holding his hands half cupped in front of his nose and looking at the floor, he suggested that since Thursday was the regular meeting day, the whole meeting should be discontinued. Worker pointed out that the meeting had been called to order by the president and was, therefore, officially in session. U. supported the worker in this matter.

U. then attempted to get the group to decide on a day for the party which he said could be made flexible since it was at his house. No definite date could be arrived at and U. then suggested that the president take a poll. R. referred this matter to T. as secretary. T. plucked at hair on his wrist and did nothing. R. then said to Sgt. U., "You asked for it, you do it."

During this exchange in failure to operate between R. and T. there was a snicker—I believe by X.—but this was lost in the general gentleness of the others in support of a move by U. to provide the missing direction. In short order he succeeded in having himself appointed a committee chairman to negotiate with the nurse, secured the assistance of X. to help in the kitchen during the party, set the date as Thursday at 3:00 or 3:30—or however is best for ward routine—and invited the worker to attend.

At about this time, U. brought up that the group was supposed to go fishing on Thursday. Worker informed the group that no arrangements had been made for this. U. said in a surprised tone, "No arrangements?" When this information was repeated, the group seemed to understand and no further mention was made of this.

This quick footwork by Sgt. U. had a marked effect upon R. Gathering himself together in his best executive manner, he said that the group should also decide on going to some shows since they have not been to the show for some weeks. There was some question about whether this should be decided by going and getting the schedule and, upon returning, he named off the shows available. X. nominated a Jerry Lewis picture which the group accepted. He also expressed a fondness for a Tarzan movie, but was careful not to put this in form of a motion. Group then decided on the *Diary of Anne Frank* for the second movie. Sgt. U. moved that the meeting be adjourned and this was seconded and the president adjourned the meeting.

Summary: The worker has the impression that the following took place in this meeting:

1. The group moved together in a cohesive manner at what was interpreted as the threat of the worker to coerce them and remove their officers.
2. The worker's role was clarified to the group since the group chose to support its officers and worker accepted this decision. During the meeting on at least two occasions when members turned to the worker saying, in effect, "if it's all right with you" the worker would disclaim the right to pass on whether a course of action was "all right" and turned the decision back to the group.
3. The group received the information that no planning had been done by their president with understanding and acceptance, but with determination, nevertheless, to accomplish the planning. While at first refusing the post of chairman of the committee charged with this, Sgt. U., after the exchange between R. and T. betraying their inability to operate, quickly secured his legal appointment as chairman and moved to get the planning under way.
4. This latter action seemed to galvanize R. into appropriate activity as president for the first time in some weeks (his proposal as to movies).
5. Every member, except W., had something to say at some time during the meeting, although S. was drawn in only to agree with a proposal of someone else.

It is of more than passing interest that these two presidents did not respond to therapy, neither did they respond to the efforts of their fellow-patients to help them learn their roles in the patient group.

TWO PATIENTS

Two quite different examples of the manner in which treatment is altered to fit the needs of individual cases are presented with on-the-spot and verbatim reports used illustratively.

THE THERAPEUTIC EFFECT of the milieu may be conceptualized in terms of support and limit-setting. Within this framework it should present to the patient a timely and expectant-of-success support to his efforts at re-establishing continuity in his life; at the same time firmly setting practical limits to the amount of deviation which may be tolerated.

In practice, the relative importance of these two factors varies widely. Some cases appear to react favorably to a maximum of support and require relatively minor attention to limits. With others, the reverse is true, and each case requires considerable study before the appropriate balance is found. To illustrate, the following two cases are presented in some detail. It will be noted that the first-case responded primarily to staff support and the treatment was distinctly a group effort, the psychiatrist directing the "team" rather than developing an extensive and intensive psychiatrist-patient relationship. In contrast, the second case illustrates the use of the staff in setting limits and keeping the psychiatrist meticulously informed concerning the resultant interaction. In the first case the staff's functional effectiveness depended upon direction from the psychiatrist, whereas in the second, the psychiatrist's effectiveness depended upon the sturdy reliability and information provided him by the staff.

FIRST CASE—ELWOOD

Elwood E. Samson from Portland, Maine, was remembered for his few days in basic training as "extremely quiet and isolated, wandering around vaguely in a perpetual daze, making his presence felt by acting as if he wasn't there at all. His bunk mates reacted to his helplessness with open offers of help; for the few days they knew him there was no hazing or joking, his bed and equipment were taken care of by others and they led him quietly by the hand. He is remembered as someone who was 'away from home, a mother's boy . . . just homesick'."

He was hospitalized. His mother was already on her way to the camp and on arrival, "raised quite a fuss." "His trouble . . . he's just stupid, unschooled in worldly affairs. It's just not enough sleep and not enough to eat. I don't mean there wasn't enough food for the boys. He just wasn't asking for enough," was her summation.

The squad remembers him fondly. One day they were issued foot-lockers (a medium-sized trunk) and carried them the hundred feet to their own barracks. Elwood lost his on the way and the whole barracks couldn't find it. (To which they characteristically responded by stealing another and telling him they had located his.) "How could he do it?" they still marvel, "lose it in a hundred feet!"

Admitted to our ward directly from the hospital at basic training, he would not talk above a mumble for many weeks, exhibiting in this as well as a hundred other ways his unwillingness to enter into clear communication with the staff. He made no efforts to remove the confusion he claimed.

On admission, the nurse notes: "Slow in speech and motion. Very confused. Having difficulty in keeping pants up. Scratching legs and buttocks almost continuously and wiped hand over face frequently. Had quite a time managing the pants, scratching and wiping at the same time. When I asked what his trouble was, he told me hesitatingly—with much questioning on my part—about loading railroad ties on a truck, dropping one on his boot, going to hospital, getting x-rayed, not waiting for report, going back to Company Area, moving into new barracks, being sent back to hospital in a cab to get the x-ray report —all in a very low tone and very indistinctly as though he has a mouthful of something."

(Quite incidentally, the humor seen by the nurse in the beginning turned out, in a joke three months later, to be the signal for the beginnings of realistic transactions, and in the same office.)

In his interview with the psychiatrist, his role was that of the little boy, caught with the jam on his shirt, confronted by the empty jam pot and determined to maintain his innocence of the whole matter. He could not conceal the fact that he did "know what was going on," but calmly countered the interviewer's questions with a host of maneuvers that are usually subsumed under "passive negativism." For example: Long one-to-four-minute pauses before answering a question, avoiding and evading key questions by, "What?" or "Huh?", in addition to mumbling the answers he did give in such low amplitude as to make understanding uncertain. During the hour, he used: "I don't know" as a response over a hundred times—in the manner of a carefree, but stubborn child. On the whole, he disclaimed positive knowledge of almost everything except for two statements, "It's important to make something out of yourself and be a success," and about basic training, "Everybody was coming and going and I wasn't getting anywhere."

Later that day, he volunteered to a technician, "I don't know what or where I am or what I'm doing. If I don't get out of here by tomorrow, I'll never get out." He began pacing about and investigating the ward, a procedure he was to continue without let-up for three months.

In the evening a technician asked, "Where you from?"
Patient: Long pause, then whispers, "Fort Dix."
Technician: "How long in the service?"
Patient: Long pause, whispers, "Not long."
Technician: "How long?"
Patient: Long pause, whispers, "Two weeks."
Long pause, then patient asks, "Where am I?" (He has previously discussed this with six different people, but not this one.) Later, goes into technician's office, examines papers on his desk. *Technician:* "What do you want to know?" *Patient:* "Do those papers have anything to do with how long I will be here?"

The following day was a ward picnic day and he was taken along. He continued "aimless and lost" until the nurse, walking with him and another patient, suggested a race. Before he could control himself, he had joined, ran "off like the wind, finished about six paces ahead of —— and far ahead of me. At the end of the race, he immediately reassumed the wandering type of gait." He joined patients and technicians in a ball game and, "When it was his time to bat, he was out on the field and we had to get him to come in to bat. And, when he was supposed to be out in the field, he would go from field to home plate and back again."

In the morning he greeted a technician with, "I'm not insane and I want to know when I can leave. I won't stay here."

That night, he asked a technician if one of the actors in an entertainment was an F.B.I. agent. Another technician asked, "Elmore, how did you like the show?" The crisp answer was, "My name is not Elmore."

The next day the technicians describe: "When spoken to, he just looks at you and walks away. When he comes to the office, and you ask him what he wants, he'll just stand there looking at you as if you hadn't said a word." Another reports, "Several times he approached me as if he wanted to talk. Each time the result would be the same. He would stand just off from me and with one forearm across his body and holding the elbow of the other arm, he would survey me all over from close range. Then he would suddenly walk away, wander around and then repeat the procedure."

Another technician, refused a response several times, tried the technique of asking him the same question repeatedly. Elwood came back "real snappy" and said quite clearly and distinctly, "I don't want to play any games with anybody and I don't want to look at TV. You can't help me. I don't want to do anything."

He ignored all the other patients completely. By the fifth day, he had informed each staff member that he didn't know what was going on, not neglecting any. By the end of the week, Elwood had made his role as clear as he could.

THE FAMILY

Elwood's mother was a figure of mystery herself, quite as uncommunicative, as suspicious certainly, and probably more expert at the use of the projection mechanism than he. Questions were treated as, "You put me through the third degree. You ask things I don't see how it could help him any."

Elwood was an only child, born when she was forty, "a change-of-life baby" after eleven years of marriage. She says there were "complications" during the pregnancy and after the delivery; he had to stay in the hospital two months because of stomach valve trouble (no surgery), and because her sister was "too nervous" to care for him and she couldn't herself because she was "too sore from the delivery and the stitches."

She would not tell about the early years, presumably afraid of revealing some secret about the husband. He was "hospitalized" for two years prior to his death when the patient was three or four. She hinted at cancer, but the community hinted at a mental illness with his "burning himself up" and suicide.

Elwood was "cared for" by her sister while she worked in a laundry where she has been "martyring" steadily for eighteen years. In the house, Elwood was "shushed" from the beginning, a small, weakly, potentially noisy intruder where his aunt was 48 years his senior and the boarder whom she eventually married some 55 years his senior. He was friendless and required to stay home with radio and later TV. "I just wanted him home. If he wasn't happy it wasn't my fault. I never made him do anything. Anything the other kids had I bought him or if I couldn't my sister did." The toys are still preserved upstairs, unblemished and unchipped.

Elwood in school was, "shy, cross words made him cry. I couldn't tell him my troubles because it upset him so." To the teachers he was anonymity itself: "The kind of a boy who would come into your class at the beginning of a semester, sit in the middle, and when the semester ended you wouldn't know any more about him than when he first came." His need for glasses wasn't discovered until the fifth grade.

In late adolescence he acquired two friends and a job; a year ago, a girl. One friend says, "I knew him, but really I didn't bother with him too much. I don't think he's a lot different now than he was then." The other, who knew him better, thinks he was "quiet and good in school. We talked about our cars and school and his girl. He cared for her more than she did for him. She used to load him up with her troubles. She had him worried about half to death. He did some peculiar things. Last year he seemed to have the idea that someone was staring at him—he was always looking over his shoulder. His mother, she was the big thing. Boy, was she high-strung. But she did try to be mother, father, godmother, daughter and Santa Claus. Right now she's in a mess. She thinks he's as sane as anyone and he's just in the hospital because of some government plot or something." The mother wrote to the hospital, "I wish to the Good Lord I knew who caused this. I was wondering if anyone was punishing him." The job, mentioned above, was dishwashing at night in a motel restaurant. He saved $1000 in three years from this work.

ON THE WARD

The daily reports of the nurse and technicians reflected a theme of confusion during the following month:*

T: Total bewilderment . . . asked, "Can I leave now?" . . . wandering around ward from place to place . . . very much confused during the entire day, asked a question and then wanders off before you can answer . . . went back to bed and seemed confused . . . walking around the ward as usual, not saying a thing.

---

*N. will signify the ward nurse and *T.* the technicians. These reports follow a chronological order and are extracted from context mainly in terms of theme, from a compilation totaling over 150,000 words in each case.

N: Aimless wandering about ward. Comes into office frequently but does not respond when asked if he wants something. Later asked why everyone knew everything about him.

T: Didn't have anything to say all day . . . shows quite a bit of confusion at times, tried to go with the patients from another ward . . . still seems to be lost, tries to talk but just looks at you and turns away. Had to push him to get him started to mess hall. Later came into office and asked if he could talk to someone and I said, 'Yes, sit down and we'll talk' and he sat down but wouldn't say anything. Sat there awhile and then he got up and left . . . very confused, pacing . . . said he is going to die . . . made his bed quickly this morning for a change. Then talked a lot, for him, saying he had always felt left out of things and found it hard to mix like most fellows. Said this was one reason he enlisted in the Army, that it would give him an opportunity to meet and mix with other fellows. At home he could talk to his mother or aunt when he felt lonely. At first he liked basic training in the Army but began to realize that the other fellows never asked him to go along. Broke into tears and then said he is lonely here and doesn't think the other patients want any part of him . . . seems to always want to go in the opposite direction from the rest of the group.

N: Continues wandering and unresponsive. In gym the Physical Reconditioning Technician offered him the badminton racket and asked him to play in his place. Elwood looked at the tech, at me, at the other players and finally took the racket and went to the court. He returned the bird when it came within his reach, but made no effort to go after it when it didn't. Later he wrote a letter to his mother and brought it to me without an envelope; got an envelope when I told him where they were (have told him twice before) and addressed it, but got that wrong too.

T: Walks behind people, watching and touching everything. Took socks and shoes belonging to two other patients. Kept staring at another patient and got cussed out. Said he wants to know what this is all about and if he is going to die. . . . I have been staying with him the past few days, when he walks, I walk with him and when he sits I sit with him. He has tried to talk several times but when he starts, he stops and just shakes his head and then just looks at me. . . . While eating lunch he quite distinctly said, "My name is Elwood Samson". . . . This evening he came to me and asked if he could have his name changed. He said he didn't have any money and would like his name to be McGraw. While he was taking his shower, he asked another patient about his name, later followed him around and asked him if he were his doctor. The other patient laughed.

N: In and out of the office. Usually comes over to my desk and looks at
all the papers on it. When I ask if I can help him, he just looks at
me and then wanders out. In group therapy when the doctor asked
him if he would like to ask or tell us anything, he just mumbled and
we couldn't hear. The patient next to him said that he asked if we
would tell him what the score was.

T: Seems confused. Thinks the FBI is coming to kill him. Refuses to
go to the mess hall and we have to pull or push him to every activity.

During this period, Elwood did not speak to me either. When
I invited him into my office, or sat with him on the ward, he
treated me as just another member of the staff, to be barely
tolerated and resisted whenever possible. Not able to talk with
him, I had no choice but to work through my staff. We first of
all investigated the meaning of the word, "confusion." I pointed
out to them that it was the most widely-used descriptive term
and had already scored over a hundred repetitions in their
notes. What could it mean?

The discussions, following the pattern described earlier (pp.
8ff), led us in the direction of considering whether Elwood
was the sole rightful possessor of the appellation, "confused."
When it was evident that the staff was also "confused" about
Elwood, it then became possible to perceive that "confusion"
was a part of the relationship between Elwood and the staff,
and by that token a problem for both. Arriving at this concept,
the staff quickly began to compare notes and concluded that he
was "working very hard at it." What interested us all was that
suffering from as much "confusion" as he claimed he didn't
seem to be "suffering." He could and did laugh at times, and
had been noted to quickly choke it off, when he did. Nevertheless, the group consensus was that he was seriously "sick,"
but that it simply could not accept such a miserable picture of
a young man as he presented, i.e., a "rude, insolent, mixed-up
know-nothing," as truly representative. The ensuing decision,
to increase expectancies of adequate performance, ushered in
the second phase of his treatment and clarified the hidden
hostility in his behavior for all concerned.

The result of the staff's increased expectancy brought into focus a strong and sturdy resistance from the patient in which his attempt to define his own role reached desperate proportions at times, the "symptom-communication" changing little, but increasing in intensity. For example, note the change in staff attitude during the ensuing month:

T: When I asked him to catch up with the other fellows, he said, "Who in the hell do you think you are? I don't have to take orders from you or any of the rest here.". . . . First said he didn't want to go for a walk. Then said he wanted a hot dog, but when I took him off the ward he would not move and so I had to push him back. He just stood outside the door and would not go down the stairs or back to the ward. I think he misses not being pushed.

N: In the office more frequently today, reading the bulletin board, examining pass book. Would not leave several times when I asked him to and I had to assist him out. Went to meals but would not go to Occupational Therapy. During this hour came into office and asked me if he could go "over there." I asked where "over there" was and he replied, "Red Cross Building." I told him this was the O.T. hour and since he didn't go there, he would not be able to go any other place at this time. When the evening techs came on duty he came into the office. I asked them if he had had a shower during the weekend. He had not. Before I left the ward, I told him I expected him to take a shower. He said he didn't need one. I pointed out that he had not bathed since Thursday and while he was in the Army he was expected to bathe more frequently. I told him if he did not shower this evening, we could only assume he was not well enough to do so and we would have to assist him to shower or shower him. He muttered that he could shower himself, so I repeated that we expected him to do so then. He glared at me and said he didn't want to take a shower. I told the techs in front of the patient that if he didn't shower in a reasonable time, they were to shower him.

T: I asked him finally to take his shower. After awhile, he came in, pulled off his clothing and just stood under the water. So I told him to use the soap and he didn't. So the other tech and I got busy and washed him. He put up a little resistance, but then went ahead and dried himself. We didn't have to say anything more to him.

T: He took a pack of cards out of the drawer and I asked, "Do you play cards, Elwood?" He said, "No, I don't know anything about them." When he laid the deck down, I picked it up, sorted out the ace of hearts and asked what it was. He told me. After doing this with several other cards, I laid out two poker hands, one with three 8's and a pair of 3's; the other with three 6's and a pair of aces; and asked, "Which is the best hand, Elwood?" He grinned and said, "Anybody knows that" and pointed to the hand of 8's and 3's. I said, "Do you believe we are trying to help you?" He said, "I don't know, I guess so, sometimes."

T: When I was ready to take Solomon for a walk, Samson asked me if he could go along. The nurse told him that if he went he would have to keep up and not lag behind. When we got to the door, he stopped. I said, "Samson are you going or not?" He just stood there and looked at me. Then the nurse came up and asked if he were going or not. He just stood there. So, she told me to bring him back. I had to pull him back and he kept saying, "I'm going, I'm going." She told him, "I told you if you stopped and didn't keep up with the technicians they were to bring you back and you didn't even try to keep up, so you'll have to stay on the ward." He said, "You didn't even give me a chance. I wish you'd make up your mind." He went to the next meal without any trouble.

N: Immediately after breakfast, Sgt. ——— came into the office with plant out of its pot and said patient had thrown a chair, broken the pot and a window section; that he became angry when the tech had commented that he did not think patient wanted to leave here because of his uncooperativeness. I asked him to bring Samson to office and asked him why he felt he had to throw a chair. He muttered something about "they won't leave me alone" and left the office. At ward rounds, he refused to stand at his bed until the doctor told the techs to bring him to it and explained that he was expected to be at his bed during rounds. Did not join the conference during group session until it was nearly over, but came into room and stood by door, and would wander out into ward, never staying away from vicinity of door for very long at a time. Did not attend O.T. or P.T. Did go for a walk in afternoon . . . at least went out of the door after I explained to him that he was expected to go with the group and not give the tech trouble. Did go out the ward door, stood for a moment and looked back at me, then went on.

N: [A week later.] Quite uncooperative today. Came into my office very frequently to check the bulletin board, look at papers on desk or listen to any conversation I was having. Would not speak and would not leave the office until I got up and turned him around and assisted him out. Although I told him each time he was not to come in unless he had business or asked permission, it made no difference. I finally told him he was being very rude by coming in when asked not to. He came to the door several times after that but did not enter.

T: When I asked him whom he had wanted to phone, he said, "My girl friend," and his eyes became misty. I told him he had to have the doctor's permission to make a phone call. He said "Doctor, what doctor?" I told him, and he said, "He's not my doctor."

When we were walking back from the Red Cross one of the other techs said something to him about being sick. He practically shouted back, "Who's sick? Damned if I'm sick." Later, just before the evening meal, he was standing by his cabinet and I was sitting on his chair. He reached into his cabinet and brought out a stack of letters and while he was holding them, I think I heard him say, "I'm sick, so damned sick."

He fought the battle for identification with a persistence that earned him new respect in the eyes of the entire staff. He was indeed a worthy adversary and the nurse and he were particularly fond of each other in their struggle, as she reveals: "I told him he was too sick to have a pass. He insisted he was not. I then told him that since he would not talk to us or do anything that was expected of him, went the wrong way all the time, could apparently not even remember to stay out of the doctor's or my office when he had no business there, we could only assume that he was sick. That while we recognized the fact that he did not want to admit even to himself that he is sick, we know he is and he really does too. He said nothing to this, just hung his head and looked ready to cry. I added that we were all anxious to help him get better but could not do so unless he let us. He left the office but came back later when I was giving the report to the evening men. I asked him to leave but he didn't move until I assisted him. I said, 'This is one of the things that makes us believe you are too sick to have a pass.' He said, 'You mean I had better start shaping up?' I said, 'That might be a way of saying it. Yes.' He just looked at me and walked away."

New Year's Eve came and an attending technician sums things up somewhat laconically, but most expressively: "Ate well at supper. Talked more than usual today. I notice that he gets very angry when he is told that he is a patient, or that he is sick and cannot leave because of his sickness."

THE DOCTOR'S ROLE

Where was I during this time? Certainly not with this patient. He had continued to deny me out of existence and I had not succeeded in establishing any kind of working relationship with him. However, I was vitally interested in the manner in which I was coming to know him through my staff. I had gradually come to notice that there was a struggle of definitions going on. I had noticed the "naming" concern earlier; and although I had many times seen and participated in this great ward debate about "sickness," it had not previously made its way into my awareness with such emphasis.

There was something profoundly unorthodox about this struggle. My teachers had told me the usual things about the uselessness of arguing with delusions, etc., and for a short time I tried to take his side, to dissuade my staff from insisting upon "sick" as the most appropriate label. However, they were too deep in the struggle to be other than mildly interested in my questions. They had come to appreciate the patient as troubled in his definitions of the world and with all the "apparent" struggling, they were really "offering" this young man a series of their definitions and in their very insistence, "asking" him to join in a mutually-acceptable definition of Elwood Samson which would allow communication to become established.

The situation itself had certain odd aspects. I was involved in what I believed to be an essentially psychotherapeutic relationship with a patient—who wasn't talking to me. Furthermore, I shared with my staff the conviction that the procedure was essentially correct and that progress was being made. From my enforced distance, at times I too wondered with Elwood, "What is going on here?"

T: We were all watching TV and Elwood walked in and out of no-where, said to me, "Why did you say I was crazy when you know I'm not?" . . . Patient was lying on his back staring and as I passed, I asked what he was thinking about. He asked, "Why do you keep saying I am a communist?" I asked, "Who is calling you names?" He said, "All you damn people keep calling me a communist. . . ."

T: Shortly after I came on duty, the patient asked, "Why do you wear that name tag? I know damn well that's not your real name." He also denied that his name was Samson but would not offer a name for himself. An hour later he came up to me and said, "I know one thing. I never heard of anybody named Thatcher." When asked to explain, he said, "You know. That guy who sleeps in that bed there," pointing to Thatcher's bed. I asked him what the patient's name was, and he said, "I don't know. Why don't you ask him?" I told him I was satisfied his name was Thatcher. He said, "I'm not. I don't believe any of you."

T: Twice he came into the clothing room. I asked, "What do you want to come in here for?" He said, "I want to get some of my clothes." I told him he couldn't have them. He said, "They are my clothes. Why can't I have them?" I told him, "You are a patient in a hospital. The clothes you have on are what patients wear." He asked, "Why do you all keep calling me a patient? I don't like these clothes." I replied, "You are sick and in a hospital, you are a patient here." He came back, "I wish you guys would quit telling me I'm a patient." He looked angry.

T: We talked him into acting like a soldier and the two of us had him at attention, parade rest, etc. I said, "See, he can be a soldier when he wants to be." Samson smiled and then said, "Do you really think so?" When I said, "Yes," he said, "Then why can't I get out of here?" I said, "Because you are sick." He shot back, "What the hell do you mean? You must be crazy or something."

T: He said, "Look, I know I'm in a jam but I'm not as sick as some of you people think I am. My mind is as good as it ever was. Do you think I don't know what's going on around here?" I said, "I don't know. Do you?" He said later, "I still don't think I'm sick enough to need a psychiatrist."

N: Continues to come to office frequently and check what's going on. Stands in doorway and listens to any conversation. I told him this morning emphatically he is not to come into the office unless he asks permission and tells me what he wants. He turned away in a huff, mumbling under his breath.

This afternoon was to go to x-ray for a film of his toe (had been broken at Ft. ——). Became very upset about it and asked me very clearly, when I approached him and the two techs who were getting him ready to go, why he had to go to x-ray. I explained and he said, "I don't need my toe x-rayed. I never broke it. My head is more like what was broken." I said, "Well, would you like your head x-rayed too?" He burst into spontaneous laughter of pure amusement and looked like a completely different person, but after a moment stopped laughing and said very grumpily, "It isn't funny."

Within a week's time, Samson grudgingly identified me by my correct name and title, made his first request for an appointment with me, remained through his first complete group therapy session, poured coffee for its participants, helped wash the cups, enthusiastically joined in a water-polo game, playfully tussled with another patient, suddenly began calling the technicians by their correct names, passed a box of candy around to the entire ward, enjoyed some boxing lessons, wrote his first letter in months, dropped a handful of his mother's letters into the wastebasket, strummed a guitar and did an imitation of Elvis Presley, worked out a short skit with another patient, shined his shoes, accepted an invitation to go on a bus ride and laughed heartily when the technicians asked him if he could now deny being in Washington, having seen the Washington Monument and Capitol buildings. The other patients elected him secretary of the patient-government committee, and the technician notes began to contain "cooperative," "interested," "sense of humor," and his wry comment," 'Why must I always do what others want me to do?' "

During this time, I was troubled with a nagging sense of the inadequacy of our methods; there ought to be more "humane" systems for dealing with a patient's identifications than to be required by him to transact in terms of struggle—the only alternative being to neglect and ignore him. Being so preoccupied with this problem, I did not comprehend until later what had happened.

Later, the pieces of the puzzle fell into alignment as follows: He was stoutly maintaining an identificatory model of himself as confirmed by his mother's basic attitude, "There's nothing the matter with you. You're just stupid-unschooled," or to him, "stubborn, martyred, innocent know-nothing" is an appropriate delineation or identification. The staff, on the other hand, representing "reality," said, "No, others have the prerogative of identifying you. We as representatives of society will insist upon our prerogatives and fight it out if it takes all winter."

The staff insisted that there were, in fact, a series of absolutely necessary behavioral counterparts to "being" a U. S. citizen-soldier, that the social group possessed the right to define citizen-soldier and that Elwood did not possess such a right. One might say that the staff, relatively uncontaminated by a generation of psychiatric theory in which "identification" was authoritatively delineated as an intra-psychic phenomenon, could proceed more definitively and know that identification could not adequately be considered in the light of the ego, but was indeed largely a social-cultural phenomenon.

The staff, intuitively knowing that every segment of a person's identification, from the category child, through student to adult, with all sub and way-stations in between, is defined by sources *outside himself,* then may proceed. The psychiatrist, on the other hand, finds himself contributing to the confusion by his adherence to an "accepted" model for thinking about identification. I had previously sought and welcomed an intra-psychic model which made use of such terms as "primary," "secondary," "object-cathexis," "introjection." Here I found that my model was standing between me and the patient, and that my stout adherence to it made me helpless and unable to move if the patient wouldn't talk to me. Perhaps later the patient's "free associations" would allow me to reformulate in an intra-psychic symbol system, but for the present, such a model was not useful. However, data from patients, their continuing to place me in these impossible situations of impasse, contacts with sociologists—all these encouraged me to broaden my thinking about identification, so that it is now possible to recognize that a person may not usurp the group's prerogatives with impunity, even in the slightest degree. He may not change even one letter in his name, let alone his title or designation, without first going through a series of prescribed social-cultural rituals, e.g., such as appearing before a judge in order to change his name. Let him try to redefine the student-role in his university, the role of one husband-one wife, the boundaries of his sexual conduct, or any of the thousands of other social prescriptions by which he lives, and the effect is immediate. It can be predicted that first, an attempt will be made to force him back to conformity and this failing, the next move will be some sort of banishment from group membership.

The staff knew, and of course I confirmed, that he would have to become a patient before I could treat him. This they saw as their job. When he did finally accept one of my daily invitations to talk with me, he did so only to sit uncomfortably in my office, ask me for a grounds' pass and become increasingly annoyed as I asked him questions of the psychiatrist-patient type. Although not comprehensible to me at the time, his behavior later became completely plausible when I correlated it with his statement to the staff, "I still don't think I'm sick enough to need a psychiatrist."

Reviewing the notes now clearly shows that the crucial week began with his statement: "I'm not as sick as some of you people think I am." This was the first clear evidence that he was considering the appellation "sick" as even remotely applicable to him. However, as he clearly stated, he would admit to "sick" as being relatively appropriate, but *not enough* to require a psychiatrist's services. Therefore, he could only deal with me in terms of "ward authority person" and must, as he did, resist my attempts to "be" a psychiatrist.

Furthermore, having reciprocally accepted to some degree the definition patient, he could then, and then only, engage in those transactions which are reserved for the working member in a group, camaraderie, pleasantries, cooperativeness. And, of course, achieving this new membership made it possible for him to throw the packet of his mother's letters in the waste-basket—on with the new, off with the old.

Elwood had begun to talk with me. True, it was strictly within the prescribed role-boundaries as he defined them, but from my point of view it was a more satisfactory relationship than the previous one, and I set out to make what use of it I could. In general, I tried to expand the boundaries of what he would discuss with me. He regarded each such attempt with suspicion, and even some depression, but he would "go along" with me for short detours into the doctor-patient mode.

During the subsequent three months he grudgingly began to talk with me about himself, his small family unit and the world as he and his mother viewed it. To follow what he talked about —knowing of no alternative technique—I was required to feel my way into this psychotic world with him. It unfolded as an eerie, uncanny little microcosm of two persons, mother and son, defining themselves as nearly as I could determine as two insects imprisoned in a bottle, forced by the vastly superior power of society into a series of ritualistic behaviors, not any of which was enthusiastically or cooperatively undertaken. Mother was forced to raise her son, forced to work to do so, forced to send him to school, to church, to the Army. Son was forced into what small responsibilities he had, forced to attend school, forced to "make friends," to talk to me—all of these relationships to be met with dread, repugnance and a fierce resentment against being "enslaved" by powerful society. It turned out to be a world in which no agreeable reciprocal transactions were possible, in which there was no certainty, no security anywhere, merely a despondent, monotonous, plodding concern about where the next demand would come from and how it then might be resisted when located. Indeed, it made me extremely uncomfortable when I could for brief moments visualize what it might be like to be a permanent inhabitant.

During this period, he played out the uncertain-uncommitted role in many ways. He reported his talks with me to the staff in terms of an enforced foolishness which he must tolerate in order to "get out." He would not accept the word of any person in his environment as final about anything, and in this way demonstrated the meaning of his constant checking and surveillance. Nothing could be believed, nothing was true.

The change in his behavior continued. His increasing confidence in the staff and the change from physical to vocal inter-actions is reflected in the staff's reports. The prospect of his attaining Army "membership" begins to appear.

T: This, to my knowledge, is the first time he has ever really joined in a competitive game with other patients. After it, I said, "You were all right out there." He replied, "I can play. I just never wanted to." Came out of Doctor's office and told me he'd got his pass, "I know it's a step in the right direction but it's not what I wanted." I asked what he meant and he replied, "I want to get back and get my train-ing over with. To me this is just wasted time." He stopped and then said, "No, I don't mean that." I suggested, "It's still not easy to say what you want to say, is it?" He replied, "It never was."

N: Wanted to go out on his pass right away, yet wouldn't do so until he could find another patient to accompany him. In the baggage room seemed quite surprised to see all his clothes clean and in order even though he helped the wardmaster put them away several weeks ago.

T: Patient Samson walked up to me and said, "Sergeant, let's talk." I said, "Ok, what will we talk about?" He said, "Tell me more about basic training." I said, "I've told you some about my basic; tell me about yours." He said, "Well, there's not much to tell; I had 14 hours of KP and I went into the room to put something on the wall, you know how they hang everything. And this sergeant jumped me, and that's all there was to it." I said, "Why did he jump you?" He said, "I don't know. I guess he thought I was goofing off or looking for trouble." I said, "Were you?" He said, "No." He then asked if he could write to a girl from the hospital. I said, "Yes, you can write your girl." He said, "Well, she's not my girl in a way." I said, "What do you mean?" He said, "I went with her for about five or six months but her dad didn't like me." I said, "How do you know? Did she tell you?" He said, "No, she never did say anything about it. But when I went to her house you could tell by the way he looked at me. Sometimes he would not even answer me when I spoke to him." He stopped and started to laugh and said, "I do that myself sometimes, don't I?" I said, "Yes you do." He said, "Her father did say something about the boys I ran around with. So I stopped going out with them so much." I said, "Why?" He said, "They like to mess around too much." I said, "What do you mean mess around?" He said, "Sgt. you're not that old are you?" He said, "I did my share of messing around but not as much as they did. Well, guess I'll go to bed now." He did.

T: Reading an Army paper, he whistled, "How many damn Army camps are there anyhow? Everytime I pick this thing up I find the name of another camp." I said, "So?" He said, "Hell, I thought five or six places the size of Fort ——— would hold the whole U. S. Army."

T: Talking about his home town. . . . Said he can remember when he was sick worse than now and he used to keep asking for a pass. Now he's got a pass and he asked the doctor what he's sick with and the doctor said he didn't know.

N: Checking in the office again, mumbled something and I asked why he mumbled when he could speak clearly. He replied very clearly, "I guess sometimes I don't know what to say." Later, said he would like to go back to duty. I said nothing and he said, "I could do duty." I asked, "Do you really think so?" He replied, "Yes, I know I could." I asked, "How long do you think you would last on duty?" He just looked at me and I went on. "Do you think you could get along on duty without talking or only mumbling in your beard?" He flashed a bright smile and said, "I don't have a beard," but quickly sobered. I told him he hadn't told us enough about his real problems to give us a chance to be helpful. He just looked at me again in a very pathetic way.

T: Told me he had asked the doctor for a leave and he had said, "No." He added, "He didn't exactly say 'No' and I didn't exactly ask him. I asked him if he thought I would get better or worse if I did go on a leave." I asked him, "Elwood, why can't you just sit down and talk about yourself?" He answered, "I've told you people all there is to be said. There are some things that I don't feel I have to talk about. I figure that what I did in civilian life has nothing to do with my being here." I asked if he were trying to convince me or himself. Within ten minutes he was talking about masturbation, and he was quite loud and agitated about it. He survived and soon we had a bull-session going on the ward about masturbation, everybody nearby joining in.

Soon thereafter, Elwood was talking extensively to the technicians for prolonged periods, almost exactly reversing his original behavior, and attempting now to portray his concept of the male adolescent, replete with "masculine" expletives, etc. For example:

T: Patient told me as we prepared to go to the evening meal that the doctor had told him that he could have a weekend pass. "I'll tell you all about it when we come back from chow." As soon as we returned to the ward, patient came into the office and said, "I felt better talking with the old boy today than I ever did. I don't get my leave but he said I could have a weekend pass. He said my reasons weren't good enough for a leave. What's he want me to tell him, that I want to get laid every night for a week or something? He told me I'm too slow in making up my mind. I started to get that way during my senior year in high school. Funny thing is, though, that I made the best marks I ever made." Q: "What do you mean when you say you started to get that way?" A: "I guess I just couldn't be sure of myself. I noticed it first around girls. I couldn't make up my mind whether to call or stuff like that. I couldn't be sure whether people liked me and I started to think a lot about my self. You know you keep wondering if you are doing the right thing and all and if you stop to think about it, I guess it becomes a bad habit. If there was anything at ——— that put me in the hospital, it was the noise and yelling and things like that. I never could stand a lot of noise or someone yelling at me. I remember one day I was going somewhere in the Company Area and I stepped on the grass and one of the cademen caught me. He yelled, 'Come here you stupid little s.o.b. Where in the f— are you going?' My legs wanted me to go one way but I came back and told him, and I must have been shaking like a leaf. I told him where I was going and he grinned and said, 'Go ahead, but make damned sure you double time every step of the way.' Man, I hauled a— down through that area. You've asked me what I used to do in the evening while I was there. I guess I sat around and thought about things quite a bit. I don't mean home either. I tried not to let myself go but I was never around a place like that and I guess it got the best of me." Patient went on to say that his mother hasn't been in the best of health and that she is 58 going on 59 years old. "She works in a laundry and she says she has had colds on top of colds throughout the winter. She says she aches so bad sometimes that she hates to go to work." Patient then asked me if I thought he had messed the other fellows up by not being able to do his share. "There were some pretty big, rough cookies in my company and I sure don't want any of them laying for my a—. I've heard guys say that if one person

messes up they make it hard on the rest of the guys in the company."
When the patient came into the office at first he said he only wanted
to stay for five minutes, that he planned on going on evening pass.
Patient talked for nearly two hours. At one point he remarked,
"Man, I don't know how the nurse used to put up with me. I'd
come into the office and she'd say, 'Do you want something, Elwood?'
I guess maybe I did or I wouldn't have gone in there, but nine times
out of ten I wouldn't know what I wanted. I bet she really got sick
of me. It's funny now. I bet some days she had to chase me out of
there at least twenty times a day."

T: Patient asked me this evening what he should do about his income
tax filing. I asked him what he meant and he said. "My one statement is home and one is locked there in the medicine cabinet."
Q: "What are you going to do about it?" A: "I guess I better bring
the one from home so I'll have them both together. My mother
brought it down with her but she didn't know what to do with it
and I'm darned sure I didn't when she was here. Here it is almost
the first of March and I'm not even sure how much I made last year.
Any other year I had it filled by the 10th of January."
Patient then said, "I sure was hoping I could get out of here some-
time about Friday noon, but Captain ——— says I wouldn't be able
to get home any sooner, anyhow." Stated that he planned to look
his girl friend up Friday evening no matter what time it was. I asked
him if he would be able to use his mother's car and he replied, "She
has a '53 Chevy, but I don't know if she'll let me use it or not. She
never was too anxious to loan it to me. My uncle doesn't have his
car anymore either." Patient then laughed and said, "I probably have
forgotten how to drive."
Patient then went on evening pass and remained out until 2130 hours.
Stated that he called his mother while on pass to tell her that he
would be coming home on pass Friday evening. "Man, she got all
shook up. She started yakking about catching a train and wanted to
know If I was sure I could make it by myself and all sort of things.
She told me that she had planned on coming down on Sunday afternoon. Then she winds up by saying I should write her a letter tomorrow and explain in detail about coming home and all." Patient
has taken to talking about what he was like during his first weeks
here the past few evenings. Tonight he mentioned the day that
he tussled with technician G. and the two wound up on the pave-
ment. "I remember how you used to have to push me over to the
gym and then turn around and have to push me back. You guys
must have really been sick of me. I don't know why I did that." He

tried on his O.D. uniform this evening. The pants fit pretty well, the jacket is tight and the belt just won't go around him.

Patient got to talking about the "gang" back home and stated that he never seemed to get along too well, "particularly with one kid." I asked him why he never seemed to click and he said, "I don't know. I never worried too much about it. We would get together at my girl's house and her sister used to have four or five guys come see her at one time. We'd all have a few beers and first thing one of them would get smart with my girl or something and all hell would break loose. One night I threw a beer bottle at a guy that p—— in front of my girl and he threw one back." I asked him how his mother felt about these drinking parties and he said, "She only caught me drinking much once and she reamed my a— out."

Elwood talked fluently and with steadily increasing frequency from this point onwards. From the designation of most non-verbal patient on the ward, he became the most vociferous. The mumbling gradually disappeared along with the pattern of wandering about "inspecting." everything in sight. The male technician staff, feeling strongly that they must help this patient to increase his assertiveness, went about their project in a most business-like manner. Much in the French literary tradition,* they concluded that to *cherchez la femme* would solve the problem. They had picked up pieces of information concerning "the girl" and pursued this interest in most effective fashion.

Just as the patient had discovered that he could talk about masturbation without dire consequences, he discovered in these discussions that his problems with "the girl" were not necessarily so unique and by that token guilt-laden. The male technicians, piecing his stories together, concluded that he did indeed have a problem in that "the girl" was probably not as loyal and beholden to Elwood as he naively believed. Among themselves they formed an "advisory council" to suggest strategies to Elwood, not to discover whether she were or were not untrue, but to achieve his wanted assignation. Over a series of home visits, the strategy council advised and he reported progress on his return. Certain matters of the menarche interfered

---
* Dumas, Le Blanche.

with one carefully planned conquest, whereupon new strategies were formulated and the matter eventually concluded to the satisfaction of all concerned. So intense did the group involvement become that Elwood hurried back from his visits with just as much enthusiasm as he had when he embarked, in order to report the latest chapter of his adventures. It was in this relationship that he came to have his first taste of masculine comradeship, that unique barracks-room phenomenon known to soldiers wherever they gather.

With me, the distance and suspiciousness decreased, but at no time did he ever appear really comfortable in my office. There was, among other factors, a problem that appeared insurmountable. I could see that a large measure of his difficulties was centered in the psychotic-symbiotic relationship with his mother. At the same time, there was no other human being in his world who had the slightest interest in him, other than the girl friend, and I had information from a field-trip concerning her unreliability. I concluded, therefore, that it would not be advisable at the moment to aid him in perceiving his mother as a symptom. Instead of ordering myself according to the model of "therapist" which I had been taught, I elected to content myself with what progress had already been made.

During his final weeks on the ward, he allied himself completely with the staff and related to other patients, particularly the new and acute ones, in terms of their peculiarities, for example:

T: Samson asked me, "Did you hear S——? How can he tell what I'm thinking? He told me to ask you and you'd know." I said, "He did?" and Samson continued, "Yeah, but how can you tell if he knows or not. You're no mind reader. You know what he said at first? That he can't understand anybody. Then he turns right around and says he can understand everybody and nobody can understand him." Then he walked away saying, "That guy is crazy."

N: At the group session, he tried hard to get the session going. He told me later that he feels at a loss when he cannot get the others to respond, but at the same time excuses them, "I know how hard it used to be for me to talk when I first came here."

T: He was sitting with G——— on the latter's bed and Samson asked G——— what he wanted, to go back to duty or to go home. G——— laughed and said, "Do you mean I have a choice? I don't know what plans the doctor has for me." Samson said, "Why don't you ask him?" G——— replied, "It doesn't matter that much, whatever he thinks best is what I'll try." Samson said, quite forcibly, "Sh— man, I was that way for awhile, but if you don't know what you want, how do you expect anyone to know?"

T: Says his mother and aunt are extremely superstitious: "My mother is bad enough, but my aunt is really batty on horoscopes, sends away for books and all that. You should see them, if you drop a comb, they believe you should step on it before you pick it up and never look over anyone's shoulder when they are looking in a mirror. Man, they believe all kinds of stuff like that."

As he left to return to duty, Samson shook my hand and wished me well in my work. He completed his full tour of duty with ratings as an average soldier and without further problems requiring professional help. He is presently working regularly at a trade which he learned in the Army. He has cursorily replied to our follow-up efforts to the effect that he is doing well. His mother, however, writes, "He has only lost one day's work, due to a bad snow storm. He is enjoying civilian life and has forgotten the past. He said he wishes you would also let us both do the same."

SECOND CASE—FRANK

Frank Wendell Kuhnen, Jr., was his name. It illustrated his mixed German-English ancestry and stemmed from a German word connoting bravery. He was at least a third generation* psychotic when we met him, concerned, so he said, with the conviction that x-ray machines were secretly located on the roof of the place where he worked, beamed directly at him, and that the office force was playing tape recordings of the soldier's code, also beamed in his direction. He was further convinced, he stated, that the people in his office were plotting to force upon

---

* Our resources did not permit further genealogical study.

him a conversion to Catholicism and that their behavior toward him meant that they considered him to be homosexual. The plot he talked about, however, was not confined to his place of work, for he had noted allusions to himself on TV and in his interpretations of the casual statements of several passing Army authorities superior to him in rank.

The first brief medical record indicating his need for further study is as follows:

Referred to Sick Call, ——— Station, thence to Psychiatric Clinic, U. S. Army Dispensary, Ft. ———; with symptoms of ideas of reference, auditory delusions, depression, guilt. This 27-year-old Pfc with 11 months service (previous 2-year tour, 1952-53) was born and raised in Scranton, Pa. Father died when he was 14. Mother and younger sister live in Nebraska. Two younger brothers in Iowa. Previous break in 1957 in New Orleans, La., while attending first year Tulane Law School. Dropped from school, saw Dr. ———, Psychiatrist, through Tulane Med. School Clinic. Has moved frequently about the country working in semi-skilled jobs. Hostilities with fellow workers and employers accumulate and seem to force move. Now with ——— in Army, feels spied upon, hears accusations over TV, is emotionally labile, has frequent inappropriate attacks of incapacitating anxiety. Punning and clang associations disturb thinking. Feels others are accusing him of homosexuality, are trying to control him. Contact with reality is still adequate and secondary gain provides motivation for not concealing symptoms!

Diagnosis: Schizophrenic reaction, paranoid type, manifested by ideas of persecution, disruption of thought processes, excessive rumination, inadequate motivation, passivity and anxiety.

Admit to Walter Reed General Hospital, NP.

Soon after his admission to the Department of Neuropsychiatry at Walter Reed, his case was thoroughly evaluated by a staff conference consisting of senior psychiatrists and psychologists, in addition to the psychiatric residents in training. The agreement was unanimous that the admitting diagnosis of paranoid schizophrenia was correct and a course of chlorpromazine therapy was begun.

By the time I saw him, nearly a month later, the chart was properly filled in concerning delusions, hallucinations, ideas of reference and inappropriate affect, but contained little that would allow me to identify him as a person. There were, however, some notes written by technicians that told something about him. During his first week, one wrote, "Tense and nervous . . . smokes quite a bit and stays in the area of his bed . . . appears to be a pleasant sort of a person, depressed, but willing to cooperate and says he wants to do what is expected of him . . . looks as though he has been hurt and seems confused to a certain extent."

During the next couple of weeks, the technicians noticed, pacing, smoking a lot, sat down on his bed holding his head and mumbling to himself . . . won't talk to other patients or take part in activities . . . pacing . . . pacing, nervous . . . keeps asking for a blood test, thinks he has V.D. . . . would not go to gym with rest of the patients . . . asked to make a phone call, says his people might feel crazy if they find him in this place . . . stares into space . . . doesn't read . . . doesn't talk to anyone . . . a peculiar smile on his face and his lips were moving. Sometimes he seems to be hearing voices because he seems to be talking to someone. He appears to be in worse shape today than when he came to the ward. . . . He is now sitting on the edge of his bed and is talking to someone. There is nobody in his area. He moves his lips and appears to be talking and then he stops and looks in a different direction . . . cooperative . . . eats and sleeps well . . . complains about being ready to blow up, afraid of hitting someone . . . about the same . . . no change."

It was at this point that I met him. I did so simply because he filled criteria; that is, he was a high school graduate, had more than one year of Army service, and a unanimously-agreed-upon schizophrenia. During our first formal meeting, a tape recording was made. It points up the sharp impression he made upon me and presages the trouble to come. I entered the hour trying to find the person hidden away in all the words I had read and instead found a problem—a problem of distrust so great that it would seriously disturb my staff during the ensuing months, send me scurrying back and forth to a consultant, even involve this consultant in a disagreement with another expert, later precipitate a disagreement among psychiatrists* and today leave me troubled with uncertainties.

This is what I wrote about him at the time:

Slightly overweight and somewhat flabby-muscled young man with slight enlargement of the cranium, who presents himself as a philosophically confused person who wishes psychiatric help. His presentation is highly verbal—"verbiage" is what he calls it—liberally interspersed with frequently incorrect references, apparently designed to impress his audience with his education. He shows a tendency to become suddenly annoyed, at which point he displays a dramatic "nervousness." He circumstantially describes a long history of ideas of reference concerning authority figures or father images whose conversation he feels is constantly referring to him in a disguised manner. He states that wherever he goes, he comes to have this experience with those in authority, "I find them trying to change me and influence me." He refers to hallucinations vaguely and will not amplify. He does present evidence of a poorly-organized delusional structure. He is tense, active, anxious in personal contact, as well as physical examination. Affect varies and is in general somewhat appropriate to what he is saying and his mood is one of lugubrious self-pity. Associations appear to be loosened somewhat.

Judgment and insight have apparently suffered deterioration, but the patient is by no means out of contact and the insight defect appears to be of the over-ideational type in which he finds himself so beset with doubts as to be unable to genuinely believe anything. Intelligence appears somewhat above average.

ON THE WARD

Frank wasted no time in making his impression upon the ward. He stacked books by Proust, Montaigne and Sartre on his bedside stand. He took up most of his first hour in group therapy with a long rambling monologue in which he interlaced as many literary quotes and references as he could find room for. The other patients, cautious and exceedingly careful in group therapy, looked upon his monologue, first in

---

* A year later I played the tape for an evening seminar including some of the Army's most experienced psychiatrists. They eventually divided themselves into two camps. One, "He is sincere" (seriously sick), and the other, "He is insincere" (and fooling you).

amazement, then in relief as they realized that they would not
"have to talk" as long as he was carrying on. Towards the end
of the hour, however, one saw fit to interrupt him to wonder
what this all had to do with his being on the ward, whereupon
Frank produced a histrionically sarcastic apology and was
silent.

In his individual psychotherapy hours with me, he launched
forth as one erudite and experienced in psychotherapy and its
language, trying mightily, on the one hand, to impress me and,
on the other, to carry me along into some sort of idea that he
and I would get along well; the only two persons who knew anything about psychiatry in this collection of bourgoisie into
which we were unfortunately thrown.

When this theme had gone on long enough that I had heard
it out and it was beginning to come by again, I suggested that
he might well feel a need to impress me and that he could relax
since he had done so. He looked me over very carefully, un-
doubtedly caught the wrinkle of a smile in the corners of my
eyes and agreed, "Yes, I suppose so and I think I know how,
too."

Then, with equal energy but now, however, with venom, he
began on a several-week diatribe against "society." The general theme was that "society" was an organization of people with
position, and control over the valuables of the world. This
society had secret codes, known only to its members, for pre-
serving its own integrity, and this meant keeping others "down"
and "out." Frank Wendell Kuhnen was, of course, being constantly victimized by this foul, unspeakably evil plot.

Then, he had a dream in which I was driving a Buick Electra
Convertible and he was sitting in the rumble seat. He busily
interpreted the car as being more suave and sophisticated than
a Cadillac, that I was one of the society which would not grant
him acceptance, but he was going to fool me and ride along anyway, when I asked why he didn't have a car of his own. He
then reported a repetitive dream in which he was hanging onto

a car driven by his father, and for the first time father and mother and very real emotion entered into his therapy hours.

However, before we proceed into his family relationships as he saw them, let's pause to see what had been going on in the milieu up to this point.

TRANSACTIONS WITH NURSE AND TECHNICIANS

First Day:

T: Made friends . . . fairly pleasant and quite talkative . . . played 15-20 games of ping-pong, can't sit still for more than a minute. Blamed this on chlorpromazine,* but changed it to a feeling of being constantly monitored. Talked of being "ultra-sensitive" and of thought perception. Talked at great length about philosophy and Greek Gods. . . . At chow, C. (a patient) spoke of other people doing his thinking for him. Kuhnen said, "People often lie to themselves and can't see the truth, probably because it's too painful or because they've led a life of self-inflicted pain and can't change." He disagreed with C. that the Army did a person's thinking for him. Seems to have heard a few rumors about the ward and asked if "they turn soothing music on at night while the patients slept."

Second Day:

Discussed finances with social worker who wrote:

S.W: Ambivalence in making an allotment (of his pay) to his mother. Is afraid that she will become dependent upon this. His resentment is an expression against his mother's repeatedly telling him that she would become dependent upon him in her old age. He feels that he will eventually have to assume some responsibility for the people responsible for his upbringing. He had approached his mother. She had made out a list, but in checking the list, it was never accurate. As a result, "I gave up." He was not even sure his mother wanted his help now, but instead of finding out straight from her, he decided to

---

* On the first day, my physical examination picked up erythema of palms and soles and I stopped the drug. This was the ward custom in any event, for neither the staff nor patients ordinarily wished it to be used. The skin reaction went on to desquamation and later involved the tongue and lips.

approach the problem by communicating with his brother. He does not seem to want to become involved and sees his mother maintaining power by "controlling the purse." "She's a succubus [sic]. Having laid with a woman, you lose your power and are destroyed."

Two things were pointed out: 1. Rather than discuss a point to a conclusion, he dilutes the subject with irrelevant ideas. 2. He has been partly responsible for not knowing more about his mother's financial situation and seemed to be still perpetuating this misunderstanding. This second point seemed to have been better understood and a subject for further discussion. "I guess I never reared up and demanded to know." Yet, he is fearful of any real contact with the issue or his mother whom he seems to feel is extremely powerful and influential in his life.

T: Said he was overjoyed with the ward in comparison with the one he'd been on . . . . Now he knows that someone else has greater problems than he; "C. [a patient] is in bad shape and all I want to do is help him." I asked, "What about your problems?" He replied, "I have no problems when it comes to helping someone else."

T: This afternoon C. and Kuhnen and I were sitting together talking about jobs when H. (a patient) walked in and sat down on C.'s lap and sort of mussed up his hair. Kuhnen began berating H., insisting that he stop immediately or suffer the consequences. H. asked what it was all about. Kuhnen stated that he was fully aware of how H. and other big muscular men operated. Both got loud and all the patients, except F., came around. Kuhnen stated that men like H. were known to take advantage of their size; were commonly known to maul and manipulate the little fellow like him and C. H. then told him this had gone on long enough; that Kuhnen hadn't been on the ward long enough to know that C. delighted in such attention. Kuhnen insisted that H. never do this again; offered warnings that to so much as lay a hand on him would result in a brawl. I asked Kuhnen why he felt this need to speak for C. He felt they were "two peas in a pod." Again he turned on H. and when the latter said he had taken all he was going to, Kuhnen remarked, "I've brought things to the brink. Let's settle our differences in a game of ping-pong." As things cooled, I asked if he had been speaking for C. or really for himself. He replied that he wasn't sure; never could stand people getting too close, putting hands on his shoulders.

T: He was up frequently during the night and each time would drink some water, then use the latrine. This, he said, would help him get rid of the chlorpromazine in him because he can't think of anything he dislikes more. Complained that it didn't help him any, but has given the people here a chance to learn all the nasty things about him that they couldn't have done otherwise. Now that it has been discontinued he feels like someone that was taking dope and stopped .... "I didn't realize what a helluva narcotic it is. I've been flying high on 400 per."

Third Day:

N: In group therapy spoke of feeling hunted, of the doctor being the hunter, of being in a foxhole (the best), then spoke of being dead, his skull laughing at us. Rambled on, seeming to me to be telling of his despair, pleading for help, but at the same time warning us that he would struggle to hang on to his psychosis—no mattter how much he really wanted help.

T: Said when he was taking chlorpromazine he was in "animated suspension" and didn't have too much control over his body. At one time he felt he was in a communist prison camp, was compelled to go by the code and give only the amount of information required of a prisoner.

T: Spent a lot of time with K. (a patient) comparing notes on mental telepathy.

T: Wanted to know if too many sex hormones would affect his heart. Says he feels he is on a different plateau from his fellow humans; that they are all sitting above him ready to take pot shots.

Fourth Day:

T: Spoke of his sympathy for patient B. since the latter has lost his wife, his children and even himself. Says he knows him better than anyone on the ward because they were on a previous ward together. Says that B.'s case will become less and less important if he has plenty of opportunity to talk.

T: Talking with K. about mental telepathy. Stared at him a long time, then stated that he had "just gone back in time 2400 years to the time of Alexander the Great and had seen an Indian fakir tell Alexander that he was no more important than he was." Then said, "I am the fakir." When asked who Alexander was, he wouldn't answer.

He was visited by his previous Commanding Officer in the social worker's office who reported that:

S.W.: The patient appeared very relaxed, gay, even joked. The pleasant conversation ended when the Lieutenant asked him for the key to his office desk, at which point he was quite flustered. After the Lt. left, the patient knocked on my door. "Did I disturb him. Did I disappoint him?" He kept batting this around, getting nowhere and I suggested that perhaps he had been disappointed in the Lt. "Yes, everyone always wants something." Again, away he went asking why he felt like this, etc. I said, "Look, there's something else bothering you, but you seem to keep moving further away from the point." I reviewed what had happened in the interview and the fact that it was he who had become upset, not the Lt., instead of which he said it was the Lt. He laughed and said this was true and the reason he became upset was that the key represented security, "my ticket back." I said I could understand his point, but it wasn't very realistic. Holding a key would not produce desired Army orders, but was only wishful thinking. Apparently this was too threatening and he accused me of being out of tune with him and said he "was in perfect tune with J. K. [patient], poor J. K., he's so alive. I've been trying to teach him control." He was also afraid for the Lt. to go to Germany. "They'll tear him to pieces. I'm afraid of Catholics." I pointed out that there may be meaning to such talk, but it appeared to me he was using it as a defense. He admitted this was true, but said he needed his defenses to be secure and wanted to keep them. "What would I do if they were all torn down at once? I protect myself by playing a thousand parts every day." We agreed that it might not be too good to tear down all his defenses at once, but I suggested a more comfortable life might be possible by coming to understand the need for such defenses.

Despite the strangeness of his ideas and questions, he seems to be able to put things together quite well, cutting through his stream of thoughts to bring out one that seems to have meaning. I also get the impression that he does a lot of talking just to get attention. Certainly, he won't stick to any subject for any length of time, preferring to leave every subject hanging, a mystery.

Fifth Day:

N: Points out another patient's inconsistencies. Makes frequent inconsequential requests which seem to be more of an effort to make conversation of a "non-personal" nature than a definite need for the requested item.

T: Went to the movie this P.M. and the picture was about a bigamist who led two lives and had two families with seventeen children. He called this man " a progressive schizophrenic."

T: Talked to C. (a patient) for some time, telling him to buck up and everything would be all right in the future. Got no answer.

Sixth Day:

T: A very lengthy discussion about sanity. Wanted a definition of the word and we looked it up in the dictionary. "Reasonable" was the meaning and this word seemed to "turn him on" to a very reasonable discussion on reason. The whole discussion seemed to be an effort on his part to show and to prove to me how reasonable or "sane" he is, although certain facial expressions he exhibited at times seemed very inappropriate and phoney. He also stated that he enjoyed talking to a "reasonable man" for a change. I told him I had enjoyed our conversation also and looked forward to more in the future, but I was going on night duty tomorrow night. He then replied that he can't sleep sometimes and would enjoy "spending the night with you." He also said that he was very curious as to how long he could keep up his reasonable attitude which made me wonder how genuine his "very normal" conversation was. Another curious statement he made was, "Well, I believe you've come out second best in our discussion." I replied that I hadn't thought of our conversation as a contest and asked if this was reasonable. He immediately apologized and agreed with me and went back to his very passive attitude.

T: Makes remarks like: "I'm not insane. Just a blue suit or a white suit does not make one sane or insane."

T: Shortly after midnight Kuhnen was up and said he was looking for some place to read. I invited him into the office to talk. He told me, "The only problem I have is getting back into my uniform. I just tried to do too much and I worked too hard pleasing others around me." I asked if that was why he came to the hospital and he replied, "Yes, I was overworked so they put me into an ambulance and took me to the dispensary."

Seventh Day:

T: Patient has dropped some peculiar comments, such as "I know also" and "I am different from other people" which seem to refer to some special quality of his, or the way he views himself, but he has been unwilling to discuss these further. His manner seems to be condescending.

T: He played some ping-pong with patient C. this afternoon and lost. I think it was quite a blow and it took him at least 15 minutes to get over it. He did not want to play any more.

T: Patient awoke about 12:30 P.M., approached me and demanded a light in a very hostile tone. He went on to say, "You guys are like leeches."

I invited him into the office to explain. He said. "I just did a beautiful piece of analysis on you and come up with the result that your animal toda [sic] was that of a leech." I told him this seemed rather vague to me and asked if he could be more explicit. He then related a story of going in swimming once and coming out of the water with blood-sucking leeches on him. Said he plucked them off and threw them back in the water and was going to do the same with me. Stated that he was going to make me hate him before he was through. I told him I rather doubted this and asked why he wanted me to hate him. Again he was vague and said, "Your curiosity is aroused and that's how I'm going to leave it. You figure it out." Then he started repeating that I was a leech, with emphasis and so I said, "Okay, I'm a leech, now what?" He replied, "I feel much better now and I'm going back to bed." I told him I was glad I was of some assistance. He replied, not as dramatically as before, "You're still a leech."

Eighth Day:

T: Started out his second week with another monologue in group therapy. Insists, "I'm going to do my own thinking, whether you like it or not." Smiles a great deal in a supercilious manner, not as though he really feels like smiling.

T: After I let F., H., and K. out on pass, Kuhnen was visibly shaken. I asked if he cared to discuss whatever was bothering him. He said it was the thought of going to the dance. I asked, "What about the dance?" Quite sarcastically he replied, "My thoughts are my own and will remain as such. If you know what's good for you you'll drop the subject and leave me alone." After the dance, each time he came to me for a light, coffee, etc., he would address me as "Mister," and when questioned as to what it was all about, he grinned and walked away.

T: Very quiet. When I asked why, he said, "I angered the shiftmaster." I asked, "Did you try to talk it over with him?" He answered, "No! Oh well, let's forget about it. It doesn't bother me the least bit." He walked away. At the dance tonight he sat quite far in the back alone and said nothing much afterward.

As the second week begins, we see that the veneer of pleasantness is wearing away and the understructure of distrust coming more into view. The notes over several succeeding weeks further demonstrate this change:

T: Argumentative, irritable . . . very hostile in the A.M. and said that he thought I was very stupid. When asked why he thought that, he replied with great annoyance, "It's quite obvious."

T: Would not even speak to me during the early evening. Would come up to me and tap me on the shoulder and point to his cigarette whenever he wanted a light.

T: Asked if I had read George Orwell's *1984*. I asked why. He got the book and said, "Read it and you will become familiar with many of my problems." I asked, "Why read the book?" He asked, "Do you know what 'double-think' is?" I questioned, "Why do you ask?" He said, "He gives a vivid description, it's like thinking one thing, saying another and then getting caught in the middle." Says that at times he can admit to himself he needs help, at other times, can't.

N: Contributed nothing, but followed the discussion with great alertness.

T: Took patient B. by the lapels and shouted into his face to shut up . . . very hostile . . . later was, at times, pleasant in a strained, superficial way and hostile in a silent way . . . tries hard to avoid almost everyone. At the gym he did not join in any of the activities, but insisted upon doing the things that Kuhnen wanted to do, such as take a shower immediately upon entering the gym, sitting outside and smoking or wandering all over the place. When he asks for a light, it's more of an order than a request.

T: We were talking and at one point I made a comment about his nervous breakdown. He became quite irritated and told me that he didn't have to accept that and would I please refer to it, in the future, as "mental crisis." I asked what he objected to and he said, "I am sick and irritated as hell at people telling me I'm sick."

T: Said he hated the techs questioning him and pumping him for answers.

T: Kuhnen was coming out and I bumped into him. Apologizing, I put my hand lightly on his shoulder. He pulled away and asked why I did that. I asked what he was talking about. He said he could not tolerate any one touching him, getting that close to him.

T: Walked up to me after supper and asked what I was mad at him about. This nearly floored me momentarily because I was specialing C. at the time and the two of us were working a crossword puzzle and laughing. I asked what he meant. He replied, "It's my fault. I shouldn't have said what I did." When I asked what it was he didn't reply. Then he insisted we skip the issue. I said, "I don't know what this is all about." He continued evasive and left.

T: Danced and introduced me to the girl he had danced with . . . friendly again . . . pleased to be given a post pass . . . could hardly get off the ward quickly enough . . . quite pleasant in contrast to his prior morose self . . . says his attitude about group therapy has changed, only by contributing can one obtain anything worthwhile . . . during gym, played his first group game since being on the ward—basketball—and after he made his first basket, he moved so fast we could hardly keep up with him . . . later said this was the first time he's played basketball since he was about six years old . . . quite considerate and helpful tonight.

T: Worried about patient F.'s obvious distress and asked if all patients went through a period like it. "I'm not saying it couldn't happen to me in the future, but I do feel I've been taking on my problems bit by bit."

After dinner, I asked if he would like to play a game of ping-pong and he said he didn't think so. I asked, "Are you sure?" He said, "What are you trying to do? Make me mad or something? You have been pumping me for the last two days."

T: Seemed annoyed that we were planning a visit to his home, "I was just getting things on an even keel and something like this pops up."

T: At ease, but not talking. Reading a lot. . . . Returned from his pass early. We talked about Shakespeare and he caught me in a misquotation and made quite a big thing out of it. Told K. how dumb I was.

T: Keeping to himself . . . no report . . . says he has become much more aware of reading to avoid contact with other people and has done this for twenty years . . . irritated with patient G.

T: [Reports becoming rare] Told about his last duty station, of having many intellectual chats that usually wound up with the other party leaving in a huff . . . says he always chose to mingle with ugly, homely people . . . first talk about sex, says his face always gets red when the subject comes up . . . says he has read Sartre's *Being and Nothingness* all the way through.

T: Says he is tired of being babied by the technicians. Later said he was fed up with the techs approaching him while he is reading and trying to see what he's reading and related this to being persecuted in the past because he "read books and people thought this was odd."

T: Says he is fed up with all the technicians on the ward asking him why all the time. "You people treat me like I am a silly schizophrenic."

By this time, about six weeks had gone by. I was becoming aware that the technician reports were increasingly sterile and largely disinterested. Getting into the subject in technician conferences, it became clear that Kuhnen had managed to obtain for himself the role of "most cordially despised patient on the ward." The technicians, despite their attempts to remain, at least, neutral, had one by one begun to react to the patient's most remarkable rudeness and insolence. Furthermore, they had come to feel guilty about their inability to find a single area of his personality that they could like, respect or admire. As one sadly remarked, "I guess my true feelings are that he's just a stuck-up slob, I mean snob."

HIS WORK ASSOCIATES

In the meanwhile, one of the research field teams* had been to Kuhnen's previous duty station, where they had conducted a series of tape-recorded individual and group interviews with those who knew him. They had organized their material and presented a report, part of which follows:

Kuhnen's Relationships

He was regarded by his barracks mates as a quiet and reserved individual who kept to himself. Not a single person considered him "my friend," and the only relationships he did have were argumentative. In these barracks debates, Kuhnen would "take it more seriously," than others, i. e., act as if his whole integrity were being debated, rather than just the topic.

His behavior reflected a bid to be regarded as different from others. First, he carried a "big book" *wherever he went;* Sartre's *Being and Nothingness* was noted by everybody. Second, he pronounced certain words "in his own way." This was not an accent or excessive attention to correctness of pronounciation, but rather a "private" inflection. Third, he maintained a schedule that was different. He often slept for a few hours after returning from work, then later in the evening, when his barrack mates had gone to bed, he took a book and went elsewhere to read.

One of the men in the barracks (B. A. with a major in philosophy) regarded him as a "pseudo-intellectual," noting that

---

* Jason Aronson, M.D., Psychiatrist, and Steven Polgar, Ph.D., Anthropologist.

Kuhnen discussed philosophy with others, but avoided the topic with him.

An over-control was also noted. Not only did he provide a paucity of information to his fellows about himself, but while playing bridge, which he did well, he did not show the usual annoyance when his partner made an obvious mistake.

Performance

During his nine months of work in the office, the lieutenant reports, "He was the best private who ever worked for me. He was almost indispensable in the office—did the work of two men." The enlisted men and the sergeant who worked in the same office, less enthusiastically, agreed, adding that he did a good job whether it was clerical, making drawings or producing a chart. They had all encouraged him to apply for OCS (Officer's Candidate School).

Events Leading to Hospitalization

They knew he had a letter from his mother asking that he visit her at Christmas, that he did have sufficient leave-time to do so and sufficient money, but that he had told them otherwise. He was active, jovial and helpful at an office Christmas party. The next day, in a ping-pong game, he made mistakes in adding his score to his opponent's—highly unusual.

Several days later he asked for a day off, stating he was "not feeling well." On the day before New Year, he had accepted the invitation of a fellow soldier to visit with his family over the holidays. On the train he discovered that this soldier's father was a retired Army Lt. Colonel. He began to shake, told his friend that he had "French's disease" and instead of visiting, got on a return train and went back to his barracks. After the holidays, he was seen in the dispensary with a cold and fever of 99+. On return to work, he told the lieutenant, "I need psychiatric help." This eventuated in his hospitalization.

Crises

The projected visit with apparent concern over the rank of his fellow soldier's father led him to escape from the situation.

He had two weeks earlier requested a transfer to Germany, wanting to get somewhere that was quiet and without too much responsibility. Again, an attempted escape.

The urging of his fellows that he apply for OCS threatened to expose his guilty secret about a previous psychotic break.

There was something threatening to him in his mother's request for a Christmas visit.

"Psychiatric help" provided the sought-after escape from the situation.

PSYCHOTHERAPY IN THE OFFICE

By this time, I was beginning to understand some of the meaning in his original complaint about authority-figures, "I find them trying to change me and influence me." For indeed, now I could see that he was partially correct. He was setting up such a situation with me.

In his individual therapy hours with me he was as assiduous, hard-working and clever as could be, "doing the work of two men." At the same time, he was engaged in an attempt to demean my staff in my eyes, and spread dissension among them as if he were engaged in a competitive rivalry with them for my affections.

Now the long monologues in group therapy, the attempts to outshine everyone else, the constant competitiveness and the absolute absence of friendliness with his fellows was beginning to make sense.

I postulated to myself that what had repetitively occurred was that each "boss" had recognized his ability, but at the same time, noticed that his relationships with his fellows were so self-defeating and anxiety-producing as to require correction. It was the attempted correction on the part of the interested authority that he was referring to in, "I find them trying to change me and influence me."

What to do about it? That was my problem. For one thing, I did not want to make an interpretation to this effect until I was more certain of my ground and until I could get a better idea of the infantile conflict that I reasoned was being constantly reenacted. However, at the same time, his situation on the ward was steadily worsening, his anxiety rising along with it, and I could not seem to find a method to help the technicians to deal with him more effectively.

So, I took the problem to my consultant. We spent several hours on it over a few weeks. He, too, had faced this issue before and had not previously found a thoroughly satisfactory method of handling it. Eventually, he asked the key question, "Do you think your staff is sophisticated enough to arrange to feed back to him an exactly 'normal' response to what he gives out? Actually, he is a snobbish bore, and he always escapes—or becomes sick, which is probably the same thing—at the time when others begin to retaliate."

I was immediately enthusiastic over the idea of clarifying to the patient the consequences of his behavior. At the same time I was by no means certain that my staff was indeed sophisticated enough to carry it off, for I feared that certain of them would portray to him an image of rejection, rather than the one of boredom which I envisioned as most appropriate. I was also curious concerning my lack of confidence in my staff's abilities and wondered what Kuhnen may have had to do with that.

THE STAFF STRATEGY

However, after a series of discussions with the nurse and later the wardmaster, we elected to give it a try. We all knew we were at an impasse with the patient and they seemed to feel that things certainly couldn't be any worse and might be better. Gathering the entire staff together at one time, I went over the strategy with them, point for point. The enthusiasm and sense of relief was immediately apparent. They "opened up" all around with statements to the effect that they knew they had been "playing a part" with Kuhnen, "treating him like a patient," rather than as a person. It was agreed that when he was a bore, he was to be quietly treated as such and when he was genuine and sincere, responded to then with interest and acceptance. He would always have me to come to, as I would not play a changed role in the new strategy.

The effect was almost immediately apparent. Instead of toying with the idea of getting an off-ward job, he became seriously active and within a week's time had a steady job as a part-time animal handler in the main research building. He began talking with the nurse about his mother, ventilating his hostility concerning her "domination." He struggled more openly with the technicians, demanding that they tell him as much about their lives as he did about his. He tried more openly to usurp their roles on the ward and seemed to notice more clearly that *he* was having difficulty with the technicians. One reports: "He talked to me about a dream that he had two or three weeks ago and had a couple of weeks before that, when he was really having difficulty talking with the technicians. Everything in the dream was just like real, the difficulty talking with the techs was the same and even in the dream he did not know what to do about the situation."

He began to more clearly demand attention. One technician reports listening to another patient when Kuhnen walked up and tried to talk his way in: "All the time W. was interjecting remarks about being roasted alive and when were we going to do it? etc.," effectively keeping Kuhnen out. "Later he came back and asked me how many of the patients here were Texans. I told him I had no idea and went back to what I was doing while he stood there with that humorless grin on his face. He looked as though he expected one of us to ask why, but we didn't, so he just trudged off."

Another technician reports: "He went into his spiel about how he was conned in his company, how gullible he was, how he

no longer trusted other people because of this, of his 'inner conflict.' He then said, 'I have talked about me, now tell be about
yourself. I seem to be doing all the talking. I would like to have
a mutual exchange of ideas and opinions.' He went on to say
that the techs are not talking to him and actually he does not
care because it gives him more opportunity to read and by
reading he has come to understand himself and others much
better, then said, 'Tell me about yourself.' I asked, 'Why are
you so interested in me?' He jumped up and went storming out
of the room. Later he came up to me, put his arm around my
shoulder and said, 'Brinkley, old friend, old pal, I want you to
know that anything else you learn about me will be strictly
hearsay.' I said, 'So?' He said, 'I thought you would be interested' and walked away.''

Another technician reports: "At lunch he said, 'Listen, I
ain't doing no talking to none of the techs. The only talking
this boy's doing is in the little closed room, under the two little
lights, with the man with the raggedy moustache. The only
thing that will do me any good around here is to talk with the
doctor and I was one of the fortunate. I got a good one.' ''

Another technician chronicles his efforts as follows: "Insisted
that I knew what he meant. I told him I didn't. He became
evasive, kept latching onto, 'Well you know I'm just coming
out of my shell.' After I returned from gym he came to me and
began rapping his mother, saying that both of his brothers got
sick of her and got entirely away from her, one at 14 years and
the other at 16, while she has managed to con him into believing
that he was a 'dear boy,' the two needing each other, etc. That
she always managed his money, always spending a little more
than was coming in. Remarked that his father drank himself to
death, that his mother was, and is, at least 'three steps ahead of
anyone else in the family and quite capable of cutting like a
knife.' He said that while we may feel that he is a master at cutting to the quick, she is far more capable. She writes that she is
going to have to depend upon making ends meet for herself;
that she cannot rely on help from her offspring. He went into a

long tirade about 'seeing her as she is, would like to bop her with a brick,' etc."

Much as we may have wished to pursue our strategy to an outcome, such as to allow us to properly evaluate it, we were prevented by the acquisition of some new material which so altered the course of events and produced such changes in the patient that we could no longer ascertain what caused what.

THE FAMILY INVESTIGATION

This case was somewhat different from most, in that no stable community home was available for our investigation. The family had been relatively nomadic for so many years that our only sources were family members themselves. However, the patient's mother had been in psychotherapy more than once, and she made available her therapist's extensive notes for our use, as well as cooperating fully herself in providing us with interviews, her own diaries, notes and explanations. She was indeed a most prolific contributor.

In reviewing this material concerning the family, it is important that it be read with the concept of bias constantly in mind. Its source is the mother and her son, and its presentation of the family is as they wish it to be seen. The majority of the words and syntax are directly from context and the only changes are those which will protect the privacy of the individuals concerned. It is in this remarkably clear bias that much of the problem will begin to unfold.

In an attempt to achieve some order, Figure 4 is presented, the various members then numbered for identification. The principal informants are heavily outlined.

1. *Paternal Grandfather*

Youthful athletic star who gave it up when married. Became government clerk. Home damaged with yellow paint and eggs during anti-German demonstrations in World War I. Quarreled with wife about religion. Moderate success in feed and grain business until depression years. Healthy.

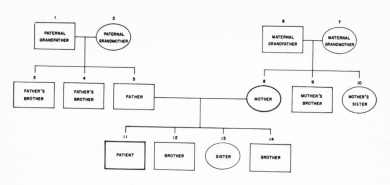

Fig. 4

2. *Paternal Grandmother*

Her parents were born and married in Germany. She was born in this country, one of six girls. She was a fiercely strict Lutheran. Two of her sisters committed suicide and one remains as an institutionalized psychotic. After marriage, not only did she disagree violently with husband about religion, but also about raising the children, always interceding when he attempted to correct or discipline them, as when they were expelled from school, wrecked cars and even when they were jailed. Kept her sons irresponsible and infantile. Generally characterized as "odd."

3. *Father's Brother*

Married against his mother's wishes, but she took them into her house where her son "sat around" while his new wife earned the living. Later was involved in unethical business practices and escaped by legal trickery, therefore, "lazy and dishonest."

4. *Father's Brother*

Mother tried to stop his marriage, but he was taken in by a clever designing female. He has become a moderately successful lawyer.

5. *Patient's Father*

Frank Wendell Kuhnen, Sr., was a little premature when born, "not expected to live," didn't nurse well or cry much. In later life he ate too much and worried about getting fat. His mother pushed him into learning to play the violin so that he played solo with the Philadelphia Symphony when he was 12, but soon gave it up to become an "All American Boy" which he did by "drinking, whoring, and tearing up the house with parties" at 15.

He would have considered the patient's mother just another sexual conquest had he not visited her family, seen the affluence and decided that he could eventually take over the father's business by marrying his daughter. In the courtship, he swaggered and made no secret of his male prerogative. He arranged with a friend to call her and report that he had been in a serious accident; when she arrived, she found him swathed in bandages in deep pain. She dissolved in tears, regretted all her unkindnesses to him and made a solemn promise that if he ever got well, she would give him her love. He jumped up, threw off the bandages, said she had proven her love to him.

They married, the wife finding him coarse and crude, he coming to consider her a cold passionless female. He tried many ways of making a living, was not successful. He was guilty of sharp practices at times, for example, obtaining thousands of gasoline ration stamps during the war. "He was a plain, common thief." His wife stated, "My husband was nothing but a heel— and a woman hates to admit that she loves a heel and will give in to a heel." All of his life he ran home to his mother whenever he was in trouble. He never ceased "trying to please her" and "never grew up" (of which more later).

He was frequently away from the home and the children saw little of him. He was a great hunter and fisherman, but never taught his sons how to hold a gun or fish. One time he allowed them to accompany him fishing in a boat, wouldn't even give them a drop line, eventually allowed one son to stroke a fish he had caught. Later in casting, he caught his hook in the side of the patient's head and cut a gash which accounts for a present-day scar.

He was eventually a salesman, probably unfaithful in flagrant ways, drank increasingly and died of a heart attack before he was forty.

6. Maternal Grandfather

As a boy, had a disordered early life because his mother was widowed twice, divorced once. Did begin working at nine to support his mother and sister, worked in circuses through adolescence and eventually became a coal broker in which business he became moderately affluent. A sturdy financial support, he did not react kindly to his wife's emotionalism.

7. Maternal Grandmother

Was the daughter of a father whose education in philosophy and Greek was frustrated by the necessity to work for a living. He married the daughter of a wealthy landowner and proceeded to mismanage the inheritance to the point of impoverishing his family. The patient's grandmother was born into this frustrated situation, in which things "should have been better," but weren't. Little is known of her early life, but in her late adolescence she left home for Philadelphia to work as a seamstress to pay her way through an art institute.

Failing to succeed in her stated goal, she married and in thirty months had three children. Immediately thereafter, she had her first hospitalization for psychosis and this was followed by two legal abortions. There were two subsequent hospitalizations for psychoses during a six-year period. Following this, no further hospitalization occurred for fourteen years until she entered a hospital to die of a "fast-growing cancer of the cortex of the brain," described by a renowned neurosurgeon as about a year old.

A beautiful woman, she was considered a good cook and well-read. Her life, however, was largely classed as a "tragedy." She supposedly considered herself a frustrated artist who "could have been." Others considered her a martyr to marriage and children, panicked by responsibilities, and given to "fits of crying and pouting like a little child." She purportedly hid money and produced $3000 when she was dying as a gift to her daughter, the patient's mother.

8. *Patient's Mother*

"As a child, I had a tragic life, growing up groping for the answers to the things that had happened to the ones I loved," begins the mother's story. She doesn't know who cared for her during the early years when her mother was in a mental hospital and remembers that she did not meet her sister until she was about five. When about seven years of age, she underwent mastoidectomy, the operation was not a success and a skull trephine was necessary, the operation lasting ten hours. Her mother's third hospitalization occurred while she was convalescent. She furnishes childhood information concerning a single sexual episode of anal entry by a small boy, and little else.

As a young woman, she was away at girl's school and "the man deliberately got me drunk on the first liquor I had ever had, drugged me and got me pregnant." An abortion took place and she maintained this episode as a blot on her "past," keeping it a guilty secret throughout her marriage. "I have never learned if my husband found that past; I suspect he did."

She married the patient's father "because I heard a young boy crying for understanding and affection and love." Immediately, she found that sexual relations were "sublime on the one hand, revolting on the other," and quickly concluded that if her new husband "had not had a strongly moral woman as a wife, he would have turned into a moral reprobate."

They moved into a small furnished home given to them by the wife's father and the patient was born during the first year of the marriage. This birth "was the beginning of the end for Frank Wendell, Senior. I could not mother a tiny baby and a grown man too and so he left me and went home to his outraged mother. He stayed in bed and developed heart and kidney pains and got some attention that way."

During the first, as in subsequent pregnancies, she demonstrated a sense of shame and disgust about her condition, wanting it kept secret, as had the two older mothers in her experience. In essence, a wife appears to be a "burden" and children added "burdens." The female members of this line appear to construe pregnancy as an "injury" with the consequence that the patient, born as the result of an "injury" was *something that should not have been.* The patient faced this crazy enigma all his life: "If I am something that should not have been, then how can I really be? I think I have being (reality), yet how can I really be something (accomplish a stature in life) if I must be guilty for it?" He has continued to act out the remainder of his problem which he did not verbalize: "I cannot really *be* anything fully or completely, therefore, I must be sure to fail whenever I am in danger of becoming anything specific or successful."

As this child grew, and others followed, she faced her own enigmas. For one thing, she had no real commitment from her husband to her, feeling that she as a wife was always shared with his mother. "My husband had a private love affair with his mother . . . not a physical one . . . but something I couldn't understand. No matter how I tried to win his respect, his mother always managed to snatch him away." She furnished some jewelry which her husband sold to buy a bracelet for his mother's birthday, "because he wanted his mother to admire him." He continually disagreed with her about raising the children. "My ways were always the wrong ways. He just criticized me, but he wouldn't say what he did want me to do."

At the same time, he questioned her loyalty, questioning his parentage of the children and telephoning her at odd hours, "just to find out what I was doing, and becoming ugly when I didn't answer the phone at once." To illustrate the tension that built up between them, she reports that at one time he only gave her $10 per month out of a $400 pay check, got deeply in debt without telling her how, presented her with a deed to sign for the sale of some property, refusing to explain, left her penniless another time so that she had to pawn her wedding ring (and to add to the confusion) "so that I could take the children to the circus." The patient, growing up in this tension, she describes as "never free from worry, fear and being driven, driven, driven."

Bickering, accusations and eventually vicious attacks upon each other pointed up their mutual lack of commitment to the marriage. "My husband went around 'blowing' about how he would never let his family become divided up. He was afraid that if we were, the rottenness would show up." Unable to "sort out the reasons for leaving him from the reasons for staying with him," the wife was adjudged psychotic during the patient's eleventh year and treated with electroshock at a hospital near Philadelphia in his twelfth year.

In retrospect, her diary states, "Both boys should have been separated from us. We were not fit parents."

The diary also tells us something about her image of herself as a person:

"Oddness almost ruined my life. My sister was odd; she never liked anything anyone else liked. My brother was odd; he didn't fit in anywhere. Everyone I ever knew, sooner or later, made me feel odd.

"Frank Wendell, Jr. has lived in four different cities in the last year. Is it any wonder that he is so tired, so tired, just wants to give up; no home, no friends, no parents, nothing. My poor little son. I wouldn't blame him if he never wanted to see me again.

"What is right and what is wrong? People go into churches trusting to find forgiveness and they come out fearing they may not be forgiven. They go in hoping to find out how to reach the beyond in good shape and come out quaking because that beyond has been rendered so awesome and so perfect that they, in their known imperfection, despair of ever making the grade. They go in begging for the peace of the saved and come out cringing with the fear of the condemned.

"When I can think calmly I can see myself setting up a goal for other people's perfection and then damning them because they don't live up to it."

Her husband's sudden death appears to have changed little in this woman's life. The financial disorder and nomadism continue to the present day. She has had no further hospitalizations, but has, from time to time, engaged herself in psychotherapy, consistently breaking off her therapy upon the advent of an adventure with a new man. There have been seven men in her life since the first husband's death; she has married and divorced two of them.

When the material from her diaries and interview is correlated with her therapist's notes, a definitive pattern is found consistent throughout all of these adventures:

a. The man must be infantile or crippled in some way. He has been:

(1) domineered by a vicious mother and long past the marrying age;

(2) actively homosexual;

(3) impotent except under perverse circumstances;

(4) physically deformed or crippled;

(5) inadequate for life's struggle.

b. Although so infantile or crippled, he has certain heroic or artistic qualities which go unappreciated:

(1) hidden determination and brilliance;

(2) simply beautiful when he started talking;

(3) a face that looked kind, yet soft and a little sad;

(4) deep-set eyes pleading for understanding;

(5) had once been a man of means and position.

c. Some member of his family has high connections:

(1) wealth;

(2) diplomatic position;

(3) political prominence.

d. Because of his noble honesty or high ethics, this man has been cheated out of the prominence or position rightfully his, but actually enjoyed by the prominent family member; i.e., he once took a stand against the crookedness and conniving of the world—and lost.

e. He is deeply unhappy and frightened and needs her "to make him well again." About a man that she married, she says, "He needed me so much I couldn't say no."

f. The adventure comes to an end when he "shocks" her with some "unbelievable and degrading sexual practice" (actually nothing unusual or remarkable).

She has reported that she has had no interest in homosexuality and that she has masturbated only rarely when "normal sexuality had been outraged by the man's perversity or inadequacy." She has apparently been relatively frigid. "Nature has taken care of most of my needs in dreams that produced orgasms." The only contraceptives used have been rubber condoms. "I hated them." The recommended diaphragm method was rejected because "I didn't want a woman probing me" for the fitting.

She vaguely recognizes a pattern in her dealings with men, referring to herself in a diary as "a female Don Quixote." At no time, however, is there evidence of insight into the rescue fantasy under whose aegis she has apparently lived out her life.

9. *The Mother's Brother*

Ran away during adolescence and has disappeared.

10. *The Mother's Sister*

Unmarried. Frequently cared for the children during the patient's family's troubles. Took a trip to Italy to paint; rarely gainfully employed, has been a part-time teacher. Began electroshock treatments five years ago and continues to have them intermittently. Considers EST "a Godsend."

11. *The Patient*

This child, never to know whether he was conceived by chance or design, was born into a melodrama upon which the curtain has never come down, and this he has come to know as life. It was hoped that he would be a girl, so that his father's mother would be pleased, since she had begat only sons. His mother's martyrdom reached a peak during the labor. "I never cried out once, nor let anyone guess how much I was suffering until an injection of rectal anesthesia suddenly brought my condition to the attention of the nurses and doctors." The cervix would not dilate and minor surgery was necessary. "No one knows how long he had been waiting and suffering to be born."

He was full term, well formed, quiet and slept well. When the doctor commented upon reddish hair, the panicky husband shouted in the corridor, "If he has red hair, he's not mine."

Within days, the new father had found an excuse to return to his mother's home. With this added stress, the mother's milk was slow to arrive and she complained of pain. This baby, however, suckled well until four months when further emotional distress reduced the mother's milk supply, at which time he was weaned to a cup.

He was circumcised at birth, but inadequate attention allowed adhesions to form and another circumcision, during his second month, left a ragged foreskin which remains as is today.

He pulled himself about by his arms at three months, stood alone at eight months and was walking before the first year. There was some ill-defined problem with his toilet training, the father eventually electing to rub the child's face in the feces he had smeared on the walls, much to the mother's horror at treating her son "like a dog." He "ran away from home" several times during his third year.

There was so little stability as to location and so much distress between his parents that the usual insistence that he learn to play comfortably with other children was lacking. Consequently, he did not learn cooperative play, was ostracized by other children and became an avid reader because there was little else that he could do successfully.

In early school years, he was a great friend of the librarian, read and gave opinions on new books and retired further from the arena of childhood games. During the fourth school year, he describes being terrifically embarrassed wearing a costume to a school Halloween party prepared by his mother—a suit of long underwear over which she pinned a diaper. The children paraded in their costumes and the longer they paraded the deeper grew his shame. He says he has relived this experience thousands of times, each time with deep mortification and flushing of his face.

Teachers described him as "a good boy . . . would do almost anything for you . . . very responsible." He was transferred from school to school twelve times in the first six grades and during this period lived with his parents, his aunt, or his grandparents with much irregularity.

In his early teens he began delivering newspapers and spent some of his earnings on equipment for a juggling and magic act upon which he spent many hours. His school work remained excellent and he won a college scholarship to Tulane through his newspaper-route work.

His mother, by this time, had been through two and was involved in her third "adventure" and he exhibited concern over her reputation. He says, at that time, he was also beginning to distrust her motives with the feeling that he was being groomed to care for her.

During his first year at Tulane, when his mother was preparing to marry an effeminate man, he became involved with a mannish college girl, worked with her on some stage props and developed ideas about the two going into stage direction together. Minor sexual foreplay left him ashamed and he confided his shame to his mother who agreed that his activity was sick and shameful. Then he discovered that the girl had been intimate with his best friend and that both had concealed their secret from him.

Shortly thereafter, he was rejected by a college fraternity on the basis of "immaturity." Within a month thereafter, he had called the local police twice about prowlers, had moved into an attic room to be safe, hid knives and scissors under his pillow and prowled the house late at night on watch for intruders.

His mother knew something was happening, but said nothing —"I was afraid he'd fall into a thousand pieces." He began hurrying to bathe with increasing frequency—"I stink."

One of his professors recognized the deterioration and placed him in the hands of the psychiatric clinic of the medical school where the diagnosis of schizophrenia was first made. His psychotherapy lasted nine months, the results were considered satisfactory and he entered the Army for his first time. He was soon a clerk, ashamed because he had been afraid to select infantry, but making a reasonable adjustment, he was stationed in Germany. He remained deeply uncertain, recalls walking for miles with a German girl to her cottage. She waited at her door for him to "ask her"; he could only turn away in shame and fear.

After satisfactorily completing his two-year tour of duty, he had five jobs in widely scattered sections of the country, some with considerable responsibility; e.g., assistant foreman of the parts department of a large auto agency in St. Louis. In each, his attitude of hostile competitiveness slowly increased the tension level until he found an escape through "righteously leaving the persecution."

12, 13, 14. *Patient's Siblings*

His two brothers have long since left the mother's influence and refuse to see her or come to her rescue. The older is married and steadily employed, caring for the younger brother in his household. Minor delinquencies appear to be the only social problem.

The sister remains under her mother's influence and although there are signs of instability, no aid has been sought up to this time.

THE IMPORTANT GROUP THERAPY SESSION

Having the benefit of the social work officer's interview with the patient's mother and opportunity for reading the diaries and notes with which he returned from his field visit, I came to a tentative conclusion about the mother's "major message" to her son and determined to propose it for his examination. The custom of the ward is to share information whenever possible* and I elected to use a group therapy session to try out the strategy.

I began the session as follows:

"Gentlemen," I said, "I too am a member of this group and today there's a matter I want to bring up. I have just finished

---

* When material from the individual therapy hours was used in group therapy, the patient's permission was elicited first. He invariably acquiesced readily.

reading and thinking about a great deal of material furnished me by the mother of one of you men. Because, in one way or another it will probably apply to all of you, I am bringing it up here.

"There's no secret about it. Kuhnen knows I have been receiving the material. After having read it all, I have come to the conclusion that her attitude toward you, Kuhnen, as well as to all the males in her life, can be summed up in a single sentence."

I walked to the blackboard, knowing that I had captured the undivided attention of the group* and wrote:

"I will help you to feel like a man."

Just as I finished, Kuhnen was half-way out of his seat, eyes flashing, "Yes, Yes, that's my mother."

I said, "All right then, let's examine it closely" and this we proceeded to do as a group, first taking each word and clause and eventually as much of the connotation as the hour allowed.

They first noticed the necessary "I," the inference that without mother's help, manhood *per se* could not exist and then that if it needed this help it was not intrinsic in itself and by that token not really "manhood."

By this time, I had complete and rapt attention, such as I had only infrequently encountered from an entire group of schizophrenics. Indeed, as I had surmised, this matter was "close to home" with them.

The hour proceeded with further examination of the problem of what "feel like a man" really meant. Questions of a pathetically childish nature came up. "Well, don't you need to be successful to be a man? Don't you need to be a real lover to be a man? I always thought it meant you had to satisfy the woman."

I reached on the table for a coffee cup, held it up and said, "Tell me, if you can, how could anyone help this coffee cup to feel like a coffee cup?"

Kuhnen by this time was nearly standing in his excitement, "I get it, I get it," he said, "It's a non-sequitur, that's what it is."

---

* Only in retrospect do I notice that I too had been, to a degree, caught up in the melodrama.

I suggested that he consider it his job to be clear about what he meant to everyone in the room. He explained, "It has no real meaning. It's just words strung together so that it looks like meaning, but it really isn't."

I could see what he was getting at, so asked if it couldn't have an effect anyway and by that token have a kind of meaning. One of the other patients suddenly interrupted, "Well what is a man anyway?"

"Well," I replied, "the best I can do is to say that a man is a grown-up male human."

"Yes, but then what is really maleness?"

"Again, the best I can say is that maleness is the possession of a penis that works."

There was quite a silence and then Kuhnen spoke, "I just can't believe it. She had to make me doubt what I am so that she could be necessary. It's so clear. I know it's right. But how could I have been so stupid? Twenty-seven years!"

I didn't feel I could answer that question, and so I said nothing.

THE FINAL WEEKS

The aforementioned group therapy session apparently had a salutary effect upon the patient. His sensitiveness decreased and he began taking week-end passes into town, and found a willing young woman with whom to play tennis in the early evenings.

Individual therapy sessions concerned themselves largely with his mother. I had elected to chip away at the characterological mode of the competitive-persecutory attitudes so clearly shared by the patient and his mother with the aim of making them appear symptomatic to him, in lieu of the "that's just the way I am" characterological system of defenses he had used. My efforts appeared to be somewhat successful in that he was increasingly able to view his mother's behavior as sick, rather than express "righteous indignation."

Within ten days after the crucial group therapy session he was waiting at my office door at the end of a day. He was intense as he asked, "May I see you? I've got something important." No emergency was evident and since I was now wary of melodrama, I suggested he wait an hour while I saw a resident, whom I had scheduled. He handled it well. When I saw him, he walked straightway into the office, sat without invitation in his usual "therapy" chair and stated:

"I think I've got it. I'm sure, really. What I've been doing all these years."

"Tell me," I encouraged.

"I've been getting revenge on society for the death of my father."

I had him repeat it while I copied it verbatim and asked him to explain. Bit by bit he did and it came out like this: He had viewed his father as victimized, cruelly ground under by society to the point of drinking himself to death in hopeless frustration. The society responsible was the world as he had learned it through his mother's eyes—a world which callously refused to recognize the suffering nobility of the underdog. Society had killed his father and deserved nothing from him but the most bitter contempt and revenge.

As he finished his explanation, he sat back in his chair, calmer than I had ever seen him and stated, "This is the best thing I've ever done. You can't imagine what a weight has been lifted. I don't have to do it any more."

As we closed the interview, I was impressed, but skeptical as I commented, "We'll see how it wears with time."

As nearly as I can tell now, it wore well with time. He was noticeably more relaxed and business-like during the day. Shortly thereafter, one of the technicians' reports read, "The patient started talking to me today by telling me that he was feeling better than he has ever felt." "Two or three more week-end passes and some leave and psst—I'll be out of here." I asked what he thought was making him feel so much better. He replied, "I found out I could chit chat. Outside on pass that is. I was beginning to wonder." I asked what he meant by chit chat and he explained it was small talk like we were doing at present . . . He talked about a girl he had met at a week-end dance, how she was a good listener and how he had made arrangements to see her again.

He reported his new understanding at a group therapy session. The group seemed to understand him fairly well until one asked him what difference it made. He tried manfully to explain "I just don't have to do it any more." Again and again they questioned this, their incredulity increasingly clear as he struggled to get his point across. Eventually we concluded that part of the trouble was that he was talking about a change in himself and most of the patients didn't like this idea, preferring to hope for a change in others.

Two days later, he reported another experience in group therapy. "Yesterday I saw what a street looked like for the first time in my life—the houses, the lawns, the trees. All my life, I guess I've never noticed—a street was just something I used to get from here to there. In a hurry too."

The following week he approached me about returning to duty. I asked for an explanation. He replied, "I'm just into my sixth month. I feel fine and ready to go back to work. There's not much point in staying on the ward because I've loused myself up with the technicians so much that it would take months to repair the damage." I suggested we both think it over and discuss it further.

Certainly I needed time to think. I was dissatisfied. There were, at least, half-a-dozen areas that I felt should be understood further. His major interpretation hadn't impressed me as it had him. However, he apparently had what he wanted, was recovered from the symptoms which brought about his hospitalization and, as far as I could determine, more capable of social integration than he had been.

I called him into my office and posed the toughest hypothetical question I could work out. "Suppose you are on duty somewhere and your Commanding Officer calls you in to tell you that he has received letters from your mother stating that you refuse to write her, she's destitute and you won't send her money. What would you do?"

"I would tell him about her," he replied, after long consideration, "and I would tell him that both therapists I have had, you and Dr. Blythe at Tulane, have agreed that I have problems enough of my own, and that her problems are hers, not mine."

"Suppose then," I went on, "that a month later, your C.O. tells you that she is now threatening him and accusing him of plotting to keep her away from her son, and if he doesn't stop, she will do him bodily harm. What would you do then?"

Without further hesitation he replied, "Don't worry, Doctor, I've already considered that I may have to sign commitment papers on my mother some day. If the time comes, I will do it."

He returned to duty the following week. At the time of this report, fifteen months have gone by and he continues to do well.

Chapter 5

EXPECTATIONS AND ASSUMPTIONS

An attempt is made to delineate those staff expectancies which may be considered relevant to a successful treatment result, and to describe the changing attitudes and developing concepts of the investigation.

ONE OF THE MOST FAR-REACHING pieces of psychiatric research in history, certainly one of the most well controlled and statistically valid, was not labeled research at all. The body of knowledge resulting from the combined efforts of literally hundreds of the nation's most brilliant and experienced psychiatrists in dealing with the soldier of World War II and the Korean Conflict, has come by tradition to be called "Combat Psychiatry." Had different conditions prevailed, no doubt today it would be called "Social Psychiatry."

From the research standpoint, the unique and distinguishing aspect of military psychiatry is the use of performance as a criterion. Whatever be the type of psychiatric intervention, its results are consistently measured against performance standards which have been validated by decades of experience with millions of men.

The bibliography detailing what happens to persons under stress and the specific therapeutic management which leads towards recovery versus that which dismisses toward chronicity has reached significant proportions by this time. By 1958, the U. S. Department of Health, Education and Welfare had accumulated a list of 2,547 articles dealing with combat psychiatry and associated topics.[92, 102, 103]

Psychiatrists in the military have consistently observed that decentralization into small functioning groups, e.g., the squad, promotes the highest level of individual functioning; further, that the individual separated from a group in which he holds committed membership will respond most favorably in a psychiatric treatment unit that expects and plans actively for his return to that group. Therefore, it would appear that we are entitled to consider, more as a behavorial law than hypothesis, that: An individual derives a large proportion of his psychological support, his well-being, from here-and-now interactions within the group wherein he holds present membership. That is, he is dependent for familiar feedback information which tells him what he needs to know about his existence. When he loses the source of this, his group, his psychological deterioration is rapid, profound, and will probably become chronic.

Of similar import to this present study, combat psychiatry studies also demonstrated that the group significantly evokes, alters, controls and shapes the behavior of its members.

The translation into action appears to be reasonably simple and direct. The group's statement would be, "We are an effective unit which under such and such conditions will perform in such and such a fashion." The member translates this into behavior with, "I am an effective person who performs in such and such a manner under such and such conditions." More importantly, his behavior will closely follow the group image. A restatement of this basic finding could be made in other ways:

> The human will welcome and follow a programmed set of behavioral standards, because a no-program or open-ended system decreases predictability and consequently increases his "anxiety."

> or

> The human requires an ego-ideal in order that he may organize his behavior around a model. (He "loves" the ideal because he notes a reduction of "anxiety" following its use. He also "hates" the ideal because part of its requirements are restrictive. Therefore, he may be found to show any combination of "love and hate"—ambivalence—towards the model.)

With this general structure in mind, let us now proceed to take note of those aspects of the therapeutic milieu in this study which are generally labeled expectancies or attitudes. We may safely assume that the treatment group's anticipations and assumptions will shape the behavior of its patients, even if we cannot, in the present state of the art, answer questions concerning the quantitative aspect.

Granting that the standards and expectancies which a group upholds have a profound effect upon the behavior of its individual members, the questions which come before us as pertinent here are: (1) Which of these expectancies may have therapeutic value? (2) How may a group organize itself so as to present therapeutic expectancies?

In preceding chapters, the organization of the staff group so as to present therapeutic expectancies has been outlined. At this point we will deal with the problem of the first question, together with supporting data.

PROBABLY RELEVANT PRINCIPLES

Certain indirectly formulated or implied principles, central to the functioning of the treatment staff, are thought to be relevant to a successful treatment result. So long as it is kept in mind that certain vital points may be overlooked, it is convenient to discuss these in terms of staff expectancies and assumptions, both of which may have similar operational effects.

(1) *The patient will be able to return to successful Army duty within six months.*

This factor, of course, defines the problem as one possessing a possible solution and removes it from the category, "hopeless." It must be quite as significant to the working staff member as it is to the patient. It provides a known end-point, binds time and paints in the general outline of the operation in advance.

It is also thoroughly in accord with precedent, albeit on a greatly expanded time scale. In combat, that treatment which was most effective was one which defined the subject's breakdown as temporary and amenable to a treatment which culminated in the re-establishment of group membership, i.e., duty. Consistent with the basic mission of the Army Medical Service, it is widely and readily understood as a goal. Medically it is comparable to the Army's present-day treatment plan afforded soldiers who contract tuberculosis, a condition formerly considered automatically disqualifying, today amenable to treatment leading to return to active duty status.

(2) *Since 95 percent of all soldiers complete their Army duty successfully, the cause of the patient's failure will be found in his performance.*

This expectancy not only places the patient in perspective as an active, rather than an innocent, agent in his own difficulties, but it serves also to award certain clear prerogatives to the staff. It allows the staff member freedom of inquiry. From the very beginning he is entitled to ask for more information concerning the patient. He may counter the patient's statement, "I am sick—or crazy—and that's that," with, "But what happened that caused you trouble?" Or when the patient states, "The Army is run by a bunch of incompetents," the technician can inquire, "What kind of trouble did you get into?"

Although a hospital treatment staff does possess the prerogatives to inquire, this attitude tends to reinforce its position in allowing its members to feel legitimate in this role. It would appear to be a relatively minor change from the customary, but its effects are far-reaching. For one thing it tends to extend the attention of the staff member beyond the conventional "right to control the patient" into a new area, " the right to control and inquire into the behavior of the patient."*

In addition to providing an additional spectrum of data, this factor probably contributed to the extent of the hostility ex-

---

* The new and naive staff member customarily reports, "I asked him about such and such and he told me it was none of my business." When he reports this, he is asked in return what he would do if he were working in the medical or surgical sections of the hospital, went to a patient to take his temperature and was refused cooperation on the basis that the patient's temperature was a private matter?

hibited by patients during the first sixty days with us. From the beginning of the study it has been a consistent finding that patients on the milieu therapy ward exhibit markedly pointed hostility toward the inquiring staff member, over and above that noted on wards using other treatment methods. This factor has been more exhaustively delineated elsewhere.[5]

The characteristic schizophrenic patient in this series appeared to expect that his explanation, "I don't know what happened," or "My bowels are stopped up and the feces are coming out of my pores and that makes me stink," would be accepted without further comment, or by the rejection of "he's crazy and that's that." When the staff member did not accept the patient's attempt to close off the communication and be rejected[5] but instead, inquired further, "What happened? What did you do (or avoid) when you were on duty?" the patient was left faced with his anxiety and in most cases took the "angry posture" as a defense against it.

(3) *The patient will be found to be communicating at all times, with respect either to the immediate situation, or his chronic problems or both, however bizarre be the system he is using.*

This expectancy is made manifest by the staff's clearly and directly assuming the responsibility for understanding, and showing it by inviting the patient's help in clarification, e.g., "Are you trying to show us that . . .?" Keeping this in mind, the staff must continue to collect and correlate observations until the major impact of the patient's behavior—the major message[5] —becomes understandable. The staff is enabled to conceive of the patient as a human being when it begins to understand his major message, such as:

"Reject me into a state hospital so I can get out of the bind between my pregnant girl friend and my mother's objections to my marrying her." Or, "Consider me so inept and ineffectual that I would be useless to the Army —and save me from the feared possibility of striking a sergeant and going to jail." Or, "Consider me so peculiar and dangerous that you'll get rid of me and then I can keep the secret about how continually frightened I am at the possibility of someone's coming to know me."

Recognizing such messages, the staff "feels" his behavior as goal directed (versus senseless) and he immediately becomes "more like us." We may disapprove of his strategy, but not of him as a person; or we may reject his symptoms (the peculiar and idiosyncratic way in which he expresses and attempts to resolve his problems) but we are not called upon to reject him *in toto*.

From a semantic-linguistic point of view, we cannot relate personally, interact with or become involved in therapy with a nosological abstraction such as "a schizophrenic," but realistic dealings are possible with a *person* who uses "schizophrenic strategies" in an attempt to get what he wants.

(4) *The schizophrenic patient's symbolic behavior can be understood.*

Logically dependent upon the previous expectancy, this one is nevertheless quite central to the existence of milieu therapy as well as any such psychotherapeutic endeavor. In practice, it has come to mean that if enough trained people work with the schizophrenic patient closely enough, obtain and correlate their observations, the subject patient's relevant "major message" will become clarified and his behavioral goals known.

(5) *Understanding him helps him.*

This attitude or belief again allows for seeing the patient in a sense as similar to ourselves, rather than fundamentally different, and since we know that being understood and understandable is of major importance for us, it is for him. Objectively, it would appear that "being understood" is one of the major steps in the direction of successful group or social living, especially as it apparently leads to relatedness and by that token away from the isolation which introduces distortion.

Since symbolic behavior is a manipulative part of a transaction between its originator and others, it anticipates the probable course of the interaction. "Understanding" assures the patient and provides a sense of success in that the anticipated or desired course of events is within the realm of human knowledge, experience and capacities to a sufficient degree to be recognizable by others. It rewards with a concept of the probability of help and allows for the reassuring hope of eventually living in the reliable system of cultural roles.

(6) *Working with others is a therapeutic experience for him.* Evidence from our field studies in which a member of the research team visits with the family and community for several days, while different in emphasis from that being provided by other researches, nevertheless correlates highly with that from other investigations in this respect: The patient's previous attitudes have prevented his smoothly learning social skills, i.e., consideration of time and the future consequences of incident behavior, smooth variation of response, good anticipatory following of the course of a person-to-person interaction, maintenance of ultimate purpose, discarding of irrelevancies, etc. Operationally he is consistently found to be socially infantile.

This expectancy provides for the possibility that in part his "recovery" may consist essentially of a learning process, one in which the situation is weighted heavily in the direction of probable success. For example, he may learn a considerable amount about soldiering from the technicians, who are soldiers and at the same time trained and careful hospital personnel. They are in a position to guide him away from possible errors in the unique manner that only one soldier can do for another, at the same time that their training weighs against a too-ready acceptance of false success such as that achieved through temporary, irrelevant, or idiosyncratic means. Eventually, this should lead to "real" duty, with the accompanying idea that it is ultimately one of the best available "treatments" for him.

Further, this attitude counters the notion that work or responsibility may be harmful for him or as he sometimes suggests, "It might make me worse." With the above attitude we are allowed to reply at an appropriate time in treatment, "Work doesn't hurt anyone," and we would like to see him make a success rather than accept another failure. To the more sophisticated, we can reply to the effect that we have no evidence to support the idea that work produces schizophrenia.

Consequently, as we return him to duty we are providing him with an opportunity to succeed and count himself among the 95 percent who do.

Summing up this series of expectancies, as we did in developing the concept of the patient's major message, it would appear that they carry the message that the staff seeks similarities between itself and its patients, rather than wholly concentrating its energies upon noting the differences. In a way, the staff message probably goes something like this: "Your problems are our problems and our problems are your problems; we'll not abandon each other."

ATTITUDE OF THE DOCTOR

Interested visitors, observers, and critics have from time to time suggested that my attitude was a significant part of the milieu. I concur that the observation is correct, disagreeing only with a few who have suggested that my attitude *is* the milieu. The latter point strikes me as a profound oversimplification, since I envision milieu therapy as a team effort whose effect is related to the effectiveness of the communication system used by that team.

It has seemed reasonable that I should then attempt to state those attitudes and expectancies of mine which I see as presumably relevant to the problem at hand. Since several attempts to accomplish this have been manifestly unsatisfactory, I will present instead, a greatly abbreviated version of the manner in which I have come to conceptualize some of the research data. In doing this, my expectancy is that the knowledgeable reader will be able to derive what he needs to know about me in the way that I view, bias and reconstruct the material.

ANALYZING THE PROBLEM

I began the research in an orthodox fashion, setting up a most comprehensive data-gathering system[5] with the aim of locating by this means something unique and specific in the psychology of the schizophrenic. The model I was using was time-tested and is still the one in biochemical research, to wit, a search for a unique factor found only in the schizophrenic and absent elsewhere, or vice versa.

As the data poured in, they served to increasingly disabuse me of my earlier hopes, which at this point in retrospect seem rather naive. Close inspection of the data, and comparisons with the thinking, feeling and acting of the non-schizophrenic, revealed similarities, rather than uniqueness.

My growing concern, as well as the rudiment of a new concept appears in this excerpt from a report which I presented to the other members of the research division approximately two years after the inception of the project.

Classical research techniques, such as those with which this audience is so intimately familiar, do not as yet seem applicable to the problem of schizophrenia. For example, it might seem relevant to set up hypotheses and put them to the test, try to evolve a theory and eventually a law. However, hypotheses are based upon some kind of secure knowledge apropos the problem. Unfortunately, we do not possess even the modest amount of reliable data necessary for the establishment of hypotheses. Let me illustrate the problem:

There are theories about schizophrenia, a goodly number, and right in this room possibly as many differing theories as there are persons. I have heard so many by this time that I have long ago lost count. The history of investigation into schizophrenia is filled with theories which have blossomed briefly and are now long forgotten—or perhaps remembered as humorous or ridiculous. The life history of many an investigator illustrates all too clearly that it's easy to get lost in schizophrenia.

What then are we to do? To me it seems reasonable to continue to search for the elusive dependent variable. Better this than introject the independent variable—our own pet theory—and suffer the consequences of sinking with our theory. Better to remain afloat with water wings than be numbered among the casualties with another sunken theory.

What can we say about schizophrenia which will be reasonably valid, and acceptable to men of judgment and good will? This much, in any event: Schizophrenia is an abstraction, not an entity. We know it and recognize it by its properties. Analogous to the electron, we know a host of its properties and derive from these a concept of what it is; but no one has ever seen it, weighed it, extracted it, handled it or measured it. We must, at this point, recognize that we work by inference, with an abstraction, constructed from a study of its properties.

There is by this time a substantial body of data concerning the properties of schizophrenia. Classically, these are summed up as disturbances in thinking, feeling and acting. In each of these areas, however, no distinctive and positively singular items are to be found.

The schizophrenic thinks delusionally, we say. Yet the ordinary citizen does not believe he will die, does not believe the weapons he makes will be used for war, believes his love object superior to all others, his religion the only genuine, his science the only true, and he quite frequently treasures the notion that somewhere, somehow, if he just plays his cards right, he can get something for nothing.

The schizophrenic is without care and affection for others, we say. As we say this, the ordinary citizen's callous disregard for his fellows fills our newspapers, hospitals, jails and graveyards.

The schizophrenic does not act as a socially responsible person, we say. Need I belabor the point by referring to the social responsibility of the advertising industry, the patent-medicine racket?

Go down the list of his so-called symptoms; hallucinations are widespread in normals and usually not reported, easily obtained under simple experimental conditions; ideas of reference abound as do misinterpretations, magical thinking and the like.

Indeed, I can safely say that every person in this room is intrinsically capable of doing, and probably has done most of, anything that I have ever known a schizophrenic to do. All that I think we can safely assume at this point in our knowledge is that there is probably a difference in degree.

A few months later, at the National Institutes of Mental Health, at one of David A. Hamburg's Adult Psychiatry staff meetings, I find that I have extended this point of view somewhat in this excerpt:

But something tending towards uniqueness is becoming so repetitive in the data that it may not be ignored. There does appear to be some consistent disturbance in self-regulation as manifested in the degree to which the schizophrenic carries his delusional, misinterpretive and social devices. For example, if we attempt to graph the manner in which the schizophrenic behaves with regard to social norms of conduct, it appears that degree of excess does come into focus as somewhat unique. (Fig. 5)

It will be seen that his delusions are carried *beyond* the usual, his misidentifications are *more frequent* than the usual, his work habits and attitudes *more contrary* than the range which the so-called normal allows for himself. To wit: the consistent complaint which others make about him

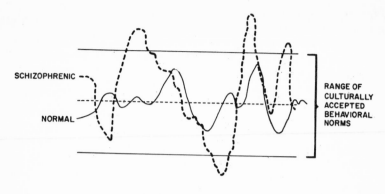

SCHIZOPHRENIC

NORMAL

RANGE OF
CULTURALLY
ACCEPTED
BEHAVIORAL
NORMS

Fig. 5

is in terms of, "He does or says *too much* of this or *too little* of that." "He gets "out of bounds" as it were, or is at times described as "out of this world."

THE OPERATIONAL POINT OF VIEW

About the same time, I find that I have begun to dispense with the customary models and am expressing myself in much more clearly operational terms. The following is an edited, but nevertheless reasonably accurate excerpt from an informal "debate" with a group of interested local psychiatrists met in an evening seminar. The group, in examining the findings and treatment results, had two main concerns which went something like this:

"We are amazed and incredulous concerning your reports about the speed with which symptoms disappear. We wonder if the cases treated are really schizophrenic at all."

My reply went approximately as follows: "Perhaps the most useful way to approach this problem would be to point out that, 'The answers you receive depend upon the questions you ask,' and take up your two points together.

"Certain connotations of the first point would indeed be flattering did they in fact apply. However, I fear that they do not and that the psychiatrist and staff working with these patients do not possess charisma. The second point is somewhat more complex, no doubt deeply imbedded in cultural as well as attitudinal factors. Let it be said, however, that the criticism 'the patient is not schizophrenic' is only made *post hoc ergo propter hoc*. No one questions that the new patient is schizophrenic when he is first accepted for treatment. He is diagnosed first by several qualified psychiatrists who have no investment in this research, and no knowledge of it in many cases. When the original diagnoses are made, there is no knowledge that this patient will be later picked for milieu therapy.

"The factor which I suspect connects these two findings is the attitude of the treatment unit, to wit, the questions we ask. We ask no questions about delusions, hallucinations, ideas of reference, etc., and therefore we get no answers concerning them. As a consequence, the case reports, and notes, contain a paucity of the material which usually fills the hospital record of the schizophrenic.

"The entire unit is trained to take the step which carries it past the defensiveness of the symptom into the area of its significance. That is, when the patient states, 'There were fifty black cars assigned to follow me wherever I went and guns trained on me from every house in my neighborhood,' the staff member immediately queries, 'Why do you tell this to me?' (What kind of relationship are you trying to set up with me?)

"So far, I have found little if any real significance to an exhaustive examination of the delusional structure—admittedly it is a most fascinating matter and no end intriguing, as indeed the Shreber case continues to be, but I have yet to be able to correlate any such examination with subsequent change in the patient. In case I have not yet been clear: I think that Breuer's careful annotation of the 108 times that Anna O.* didn't hear when someone walked into her room were related primarily to the reason for Breuer's wife's insistence that he withdraw from the case; and infinitely less related to the specific understanding of the mechanisms of hysteria.

---

* Breuer, J., and Freud, S.: *Studies on Hysteria*. New York, Basic Books, 1957

I am sure that I am, and think that the staff is also, tending more and more to be operational in our attempts to understand the patient. For example: We are taught to define the delusion somewhat as follows: A false belief . . . without appropriate external stimulation and maintained in spite of . . . incontrovertible . . . evidence to the contrary.

"If we inspect *in the company of the patient,* only as far as the third word of the definition—namely, belief—we will slowly begin to discover that the definition is inadequate, for he will become annoyed and frustrated with what he regards as our naive stupidity in interpreting his meaning. Eventually, he may explain as one did: "I said you were trying to kill me because I had to gain your attention and I figured it would work. I had no choice. I had to make it look good or you wouldn't have let me talk to you." Others have demonstrated an angry frustration, 'Surely you are not stupid enough to really believe that I believe I am Jesus Christ.' Others explain it as a monstrous joke which they play upon the staff to certify their position as dealing with a collection of fools.

"As for myself, I cannot say that I accept these oversimplified explanations any more readily than I do the definition I was taught as a student. I am not unaware that all beliefs may well be called delusions.* The point I wish to make is that the statement of a belief may be designed to evoke a response from another and/or state a position regarding others.

"More specifically in regard to the patient-therapist relationship, Bachrach[7] has suggested an alternate definition, 'a delusion is an idea expressed by the patient which the therapist may be deluded into taking literally.' The operational definition being used in our work would go something like this: A delusion is a statement made by a person for a purpose not stated in the context, presumably designed to evoke a response or state a position differing from the conventional."

---

* Masserman, J. H.: *The Ur Defenses of Mankind.* In *The Practice of Dynamic Psychiatry.* Philadelphia, W. B. Saunders, 1955.

THE LATEST CONCEPT

In late 1959 I had the good fortune of attending a scientific symposium sponsored by RISE* during which a distinguished group of researchers discussed ongoing projects as well as indications for future planning. I was heartened by the progress being made and pleased with the knowledge that so many esteemed persons were so active in this provocative field. My small contribution included the operational differentiation, after 90 days of hospitalization, of the patient who will respond to treatment from the one who will not, as outlined in Figure 6.

I also reported that in our series, if the change were going to take place at all, it would be clearly evident within the first ninety days; and if it had not taken place within that period, it would not take place even if the period of hospitalization were extended up to almost a year.

Early in 1960, at a meeting of the Chiefs of Mental Hygiene Consultation Services of the Army, I presented the following concept:

The Self

"Who am I?" is a provocative enough question in any surrounding, but it becomes a central issue when dealing with the

* Research in Schizophrenia Endowment.

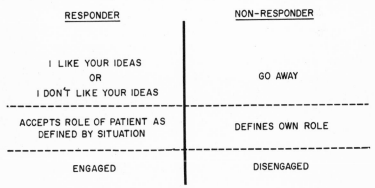

Fig. 6

schizophrenic. Discussions concerning "ego-boundaries" and "identity" abound in the literature.

In an attempt to evolve more operational concepts, let us examine what I have called "The Naming Prerogative." To do this, I suggest that you ponder for a moment and ask yourself the question, "Who am I?" You will quite likely reply, "Of course, I know who I am. I am David Jones." Let us quickly scan some of the factors which went into that knowledge.

Your name was given to you as a label without your permission by a person or persons who caused you to be born without your permission and thereby appointed themselves to be your parents with the prerogatives and rights to educate and rear you as they saw fit, again without your permission or consultation.

Further, imagine with me a hypothetical conversation during your infancy, between yourself and a parent. (Please note that certain elements are underlined. The power positions may be traced through the interchange by attending only to the underlined words.)

"Why do you call me David?"

"Because that's your name."

"How did I get it?"

"We gave it to you. It's a name we liked and belonged to a friend we both admired."

"What right do you have to name me?"

"We are your parents. And that means we are responsible for you and so the right goes with the responsibility."

"What right do you have to be parents?"

"We took the right. We wanted a child and we love you."

Most children accept the parental right to label in one way or another and the phenomenon becomes, "I am David." As they do this they enter into a reciprocal compact with the parent, i.e., yielding to him the naming prerogative. Presumably, the significance of the compact will be the reciprocity of commitment, the concurrence of being named in return for the care, love and community status that is the parental contribution.

Let us now suppose that the "agreement" was not smoothly and satisfactorily accepted by both parties—not cooperative—and a given child refused to yield this prerogative and instead assumed it for himself. He would now be able to say, "I am William" or "I am Mary" or "I am Jesus." The schizophrenic analogue has already put in its appearance.

The manifest willingness to accept parental prerogatives and cooperate in a reciprocal role system between the "namer" (parent) and the "named-one" (child) is variously referred to as respect, obedience, love, acculturation. Operationally, from the standpoint of the child, it is the tacit acceptance of a *role* which is fundamentally *defined by others,* in return for their assuming a series of vital responsibilities concerning his welfare.

Its ramifications are immense and extend throughout the socializing process. In his learning of language, for example, the child learns "that is a tree" by virtue of accepting the adult's word. It is a "tree" and not a "gok" because the adult says it is and because the child accepts the adult's naming prerogative. So also he learns codes, ethics of conduct, attitudes and the gamut of factors which lead in the direction of adaptation.

We recognize immediately that this process does not go smoothly. For one thing the child's fantasy life runs directly counter and much of it is devoted to his "being," Tarzan, mother, father, doctor, nurse, cowboy, policeman, etc. His parents are clearly aware of this as they jealously guard their prerogatives, "Come down off of there! Who do you think you are?"

The parent and child struggle through this acculturation process, and I use "struggle" advisedly, since one cannot help but notice the intensity of both parties. The consequences of the outcome are far-reaching, germane to many factors in the accomplishments and "adjustment" of the child. The child's fantasy-life, his magical-thinking attempt to organize the data from the world around him, is apparently the wellspring from which come art, music, drama, indeed probably much of the "beauty" of life. It is also the source of schizophrenic thinking.

The wise parent apparently encourages fantasy-life at the same time setting limits upon it. It should not interfere with the reality-demands of life! Junior may play "Sir Galahad" out in the yard, but he may not plunge his wooden sword into the roast at the dinner table.

However, in certain families this clarification of reciprocal roles does not appear to take place and the child is either encouraged to invade the "real" world via his fantasies or his normal attempts to do so meet with no parental resistance, i.e., his symbolic behavior becomes concretized by inadequate responses to simple needs. A constellation which may introduce the first situation is that of a seductive, on-and-off psychotic mother whose distant and aloof husband protects her and does not insist upon his limit-setting prerogatives either with her or the child in question. The second type, which we might characterize the "struggle lost by default," appears to be one in which the mother is so troubled with other problems, usually a weak and ineffectual husband, often monetary chaos, guilt, divorce, other responsibilities, intercurrent illness, etc., that she simply does not notice (or care).

In both cases, we find the child defining the situation in his own terms. He says, "I am sick" and is allowed to stay home from school without further inquiry. He says, "I don't want to (do something)" and no insistence is forthcoming. More and more he makes decisions for himself, defines the situation in his own terms, and because of his inability to abstract or know consequences, makes more and more social mistakes. These mistakes increasingly label him a failure and by virtue of his "selfishness" with other children, he is ostracized by them. Being ostracized by other children, he is further prevented from learning the rules of cooperative play and we find him largely confined to a small orbit (isolated) often spending most of the out-of-school hours in his room or wandering about.

In school, his adjustment is precarious, at best an uneasy compromise. In some instances he is "bookish" and gets fairly good grades when it satisfies his competitive needs to do so; in most cases, however, he is "odd" and unwanted, attends classes, does the work necessary to get by and returns to his isolation after school hours.

Earlier, the parent may have asked:

"Why didn't you stay at the playground?"

"The Indians were chasing me."

"All right, go play in your room."

Later it may become:

"Why don't you play baseball with the others?"

"They don't like me."

"Why not?"

"Because I'm Polish."

"Oh. Well, go and read a book then."

In adolescence his deviance becomes increasingly clear. Whatever the majority may do, he does something else. The enormous pressure for social conformity during these years increasingly challenges his personalized definitions of the situation. The school coach says, "I don't see any reason in the world why you should be excused from gymnasium sports." His family comes flying to his rescue. When the other teenagers are learning to dance, he doesn't.

"Why not?"

"I'm too awkward. Besides nobody would go out with me anyway." He is characterized as indifferent, nutty, lazy, sissified. He may at this time begin to explain his ostracism by a new theme, "Perhaps it's because I am queer or homosexual." Presumably this means in essence, "I am incapable of reliable relations with others of a friendly affectionate sort that reinforce themselves and grow."

Leaving school, he may try his hand at a few jobs. Again it is the same. The boss tells him to do it this way, he does it that way. The boss insists, and the patient-to-be quits his job.

He enters the Army, often voluntarily (with insistence from

parents, however, who are now thoroughly concerned about his lack of self-supporting tendencies) and the process begins all over again. Whatever he may be asked to do, it will be found that he personally defines it and does it in his own way. If it's polish his boots, he will either not do it at all or spend half the night on it. The series of cases studied in this sample presents a most fantastic collection of bids for deviance; ranging all the way from needing father to shave him, through answering the telephone in French, refusing to bathe, take orders, up to refusing to accept that he is in the Army at all, putting on civilian clothes and going home.

The working group says to him, "You are not doing your job correctly." He responds with, "People are calling me a queer behind my back." If such attempts as these to turn aside the issue or "change the subject" fail in their purpose, some will embark on a "schizophrenic panic." This phenomenon, when we have been able to study it, appears to contain the same quality of personal definition. That is, the patient, feeling some anxiety, defines it in his own terms as utter terror or threatened disintegration, which then, by his continuing definition, calls for extraordinary responses. It is here that the schizophrenic, desperately defending his self-defined prerogatives, may in fact become dangerous to himself and others. Insofar as we can tell, he has physiological anxiety just like anyone else, but it is this self-defined excessive response that causes others to decide to leave him alone, and discourages the psychiatrist who is covertly threatened with "causing a panic."

In any event, he will not "do the job right" because that would abrogate his right to self-define it, and the group rejects him. This self-definition appears to be a very limited one, yet the only one he has succeeded with in his isolated state. His precarious stability can only be maintained by his presupposition of group rejection. For this he asks and this he almost invariably receives. The professional later labels him "a schizophrenic."

The above operational model for the growth of the schizophrenic syndrome, derived entirely from the data of this research, provides us with a series of provocative possibilities.

The "battle" between parent and child for the naming or defining prerogative may be crucial to the schizophrenic issue. When Mrs. S. quite frankly told us, "He was just too much for us. We gave up," she may have recognized her "defeat" in being unable to prevent her son from shooting the keys off the piano with his air-rifle. The responsibility of the parent is that of binding time beyond the child's capabilities for doing so; it is only the parent who can know the relevance of future consequences to present behavior. The battle frequently relates to immediate versus future objectives. "Do not play in the street" is to the child a present imperative; he cannot know about the kinetic energy of a moving automobile. The parent of the later-to-be schizophrenic patient often battles, but usually over immediate objectives, with confusion about the future, leading to the "double-bind" [67, Chap. 13] type of imperative.

If it is a battle between parent and child, then presumably it must be won by the parent. If it does not have this outcome, then the child who takes the parent's prerogatives *is* the parent. Therefore, he *is* anyone or anything he dictates and by that token "outside the social law."

Another logical extension would be to set up an hypothesis:

Non-schizophrenic child = history of battle for prerogatives won by parent.

Schizophrenic child = history of battle for prerogatives won by child—or no contest.

How is this seen on the treatment ward? A sizable number of the patients carried the phenomenon to a surprising extreme, defining not only the situation, but also re-naming. Many renamed the ward as an "invention," "plot," "prison," etc., renamed the other patients as not really patients but rather disguised persons engaged in the total plot, refused to learn or in any way attend to the "names" of either patients or staff and,

of course, refused to accept the category "patient" as applying
to them (see page 81ff). Two of these signaled their eventual
improvement with a sudden voluntary acceptance, "This *is* a
hospital, isn't it?"

Those patients whose treatment went on to a successful conclusion and return to duty did each accept the designation
"patient" within 90 days after admission. Those patients who
did not respond did not *at any time* accept the name (patient)
nor the staff's prerogative to so designate them.

This finding is so completely valid that it can be stated, "A
successful treatment outcome for a patient will be heralded by
the staff's ability to name him 'patient' and make it stick."

OTHER INTRIGUING POSSIBILITIES

Should it be that other workers pursue such an operational
approach to this problem and confirm our findings, it may then
be possible to ask some very interesting questions.
1. Is it reasonable to assume that every child will resist "ac-
    culturation" to some degree and that "battle" or "struggle"
    is a proper designation? If so, would it not be wise to inves-
    tigate this area further and see if anti-social behavior has
    similar roots?
2. If what we call the schizophrenic syndrome is a continuing
    "fight" for the defining prerogative, does it become possible
    for us to assess the effectiveness of electroshock, insulin,
    metrazol in terms of a powerful stroke which weakens the
    organization of the patient's "fight," the effectiveness of
    drugs as powerful deterrents which weaken the patient's
    "drive to fight"?
3. If a "fight," is this one of the important reasons that psycho-
    therapy is so difficult, so discouraging for the therapist, so
    time consuming? Is it perhaps that the childhood struggle
    is relived in the therapy, with the necessary requirement
    that this victory must be achieved by the therapist over the
    patient's long-fostered omnipotence? Does it perhaps infer

that a future design for therapy will need to consider this aspect and consequently balance the attack against defenses with a specific acceptance-support which will create a situation in which the probabilities for the patient's success in dealing with social reality will be increased?

4. Will this concept help us to understand the high tension level in the schizophrenic, in that he must be always "battle ready"? Will it explain in some degree the two common parental positions:

    a. "He's perfectly normal" and/or
       "I'm taking him out of therapy," in which case the parent is fighting the same battle?

    b. "I don't know what to do," in which case the parent is guiltily expressing regret about having been hopelessly defeated?

5. Will it help us to conceptualize the important ingredients in successful Milieu Therapy? Can we possibly design a specific approach which will come to grips with the psychological struggle for omnipotence at an appropriate time in the relationship, in a relevant setting, bring it out into the open and deal with it minus subterfuge and avoidance? If so, would this process allow the patient to in some way see his behavior in adult perspective as a hollow victory which is in essence a self-defeat? Would he then possibly find a gain in giving up this ancient struggle for omnipotence to engage in the more socially acceptable division of power by which the remainder of society has found a reasonably effective functioning?

EPILOGUE

DURING RECENT YEARS I have had several kind invitations to present some of the results of this work to professional meetings of my colleagues in various sections of the country. Running through several presentations, I have noted three recurrent themes in audience questions. These appear to denote a certain uneasiness about the implications of the study and their consistent recurrence suggests that they be discussed.

Roughly they are:

(1) "The milieu you describe is, after all, the Army, and I cannot see any application of your findings to the civilian community in which I work."

(2) You as a "Colonel" must have an authoritarian "Army" relationship to the "enlisted men" who are your patients. This seems so different from our concept of a doctor-patient relationship that we wonder at times if Army psychiatry is really psychiatry at all, as we know it.

(3) Can an Army psychiatrist really be a "therapist," that is, devote himself to the interest of an individual rather than to the welfare of the total group?

It would appear that in general, two of the items could be classified as statements, only one as a question. All appear to be expressions of doubt and uncertainty.

Obviously, I cannot approach the problem of each individual doubter and it would be impertinent of me to attempt a general approach. Stereotypes are widespread, even among psychiatrists, and at times, are apparently treasured, harbored and defended no less diligently by professionals than by their patients, and I must assume, for equally personal reasons.

However, there are certain aspects of this problem which are available for consideration. It seems to me that the singular importance of using the Army as the subject of social psychiatry studies should be stressed, rather than defended or avoided. First, there is the agreed consideration that social structure in the Army is readily perceived and there are fewer relevant variables which must be considered by the sociologist. As a consequence, he informs us, the group structure is easier to study and the findings by that token increased in validity. Secondly, the Army is so well-established and so public that its norms of behavior are open to absolute scrutiny. This factor assumes high-order importance in studying the schizophrenic person who has apparently been able to evade performance norms and consequently "maintain himself" in outside society.

This unique opportunity was used in this study, and the schizophrenic person—for decades vaguely suspected of being in some way untouched or untouchable by group mores—was cast against this environmental background. Apparently it is now possible to assume that the schizophrenic person is specifically in trouble with the social structure wherever he goes; the annotated experiences of this study tend to clarify this issue, rather than obscure it.

To turn now to the officer-enlisted man issue is to venture at the same time into an area of culture-stereotypes and linguistics, where discomfort lurks for the unwary. Few of us have enough competence in these disciplines to feel confident in them and we are warned by Sapir himself* to expect discomfort when we inspect too closely. The issue, however, is too important to too many persons to avoid simply because its inspection may not be a comfortable one. The clear inference is that the Army psychiatrist may be handling his cases via directive, rather than via the traditionally "personal and confidential" doctor-patient pattern of the dyadic group.

In order to open this topic for discussion, perhaps it might be useful to approach the issue with a debate-like maneuver, a riposte, in reply to the attack which is implicit in the question, "We wonder if Army psychiatry is really psychiatry at all?" Such a rebuttal could be phrased, "Most young psychiatrists just having completed their residencies and beginning a two-year

---

* Sapir, E.: In *The Unconscious, A Symposium.* New York, Alfred A. Knopf, 1927.

tour of military duty appear rigid and stereotyped. They are largely untrained in social psychiatry and approach the psychiatric problems of a military community with the notion that a problem which cannot be solved with their style of individual psychotherapy is either (a) not a problem at all or (b) someone else's concern."

The non-Army psychiatrist should find the oversimplification in the above riposte to be transparent. It is presented in the hope that it may call his attention to the fact that the social psychiatrist finds the question, "Do Army psychiatrists really practice psychiatry at all?" to be equally transparent.

Army psychiatry makes no claim to uniqueness in its social psychiatry emphasis, recognizing that the community clinic, the family agency, child treatment centers and a host of other related efforts have all contributed. Rather, the Army psychiatrist finds himself faced with more than a request, virtually in fact a demand, from his culture that he provide for the psychiatric needs of the military community, lest that community weaken and the entire culture suffer because its defenses fail to meet the challenges posed to them. The Army psychiatrist feels most acutely the importance of the question so frequently asked by the recent president of the A.P.A.,* "How may we learn to respond more adequately to the psychiatric needs of the community with the trained talent we have available?"

The ultimate life-and-death responsibility placed upon the Army has required it to learn a great deal about social psychiatry in recent years. In general, its experience on a large scale† is similar to that being increasingly reported by community clinics in civilian life: i.e., increasingly successful results apparently correlated with an increased understanding of the relevance of treatment models which view man's transactions with his reference group and external milieu to be

---

* Robert H. Felix.

† Glass, A. J., Artiss, K. L., Gibbs, J. J., and Sweeney, V. C.: Current status of Army psychiatry. Am. J. Psychiat. *117*: 673-683, 1961.

quite as clearly related to his "adjustment" as are his intrapsychic phenomena.

Therefore, it now seems reasonable to predict that social psychiatry will expand in usefulness and influence in the immediate future and that the concept "therapist" will expand with it, hopefully in the direction of more adequately meeting the overwhelming need.

The third point, it seems to me, is only arbitrarily separable from the second. Nevertheless, it is relevant indeed. Group and community therapy techniques are used with increasing frequency throughout the land. Just how a group defines its "therapist" is only beginning to be explored and insofar as I can determine, definitive answers to "What is psychotherapy?" and "What is a psychotherapist?" must await further research.

POSSIBLE CIVILIAN APPLICATIONS OF THIS STUDY

Under the close control and scrutiny mentioned, certain points have been highlighted which may well require consideration in the designing of successful treatment strategies in civilian life. All three below are derivative of the rapidly-expanding use of and attention to principles of social psychiatry.

(1) *Treatment Goal*
        The therapist or therapeutic agency should
        have a known goal for its treatment efforts.

For example, a community might so design its efforts that it channelled the majority of its energies into an acute intensive treatment unit on the assumption that early and definitive treatment designed to interrupt the trend toward chronicity was the best possible strategy over time. Under such circumstances, an aim such as eradication of symptoms would not be an adequate or practical goal for the treatment of the schizophrenic. Theoretically, it would deprive him of his adaptive defenses without replacement by other supports, but regardless of theory and in operational terms, his symptoms appear to be an outgrowth and accompaniment of an inadequate character development. Consequently, it appears that unless his social immaturity is adequately treated, his prognosis will not be substantially improved.

It would, therefore, seem that an important goal in civilian life which parallels that of this study would be his eventual achievement of a *regular* paycheck. It should hold in civilian-treated schizophrenic persons also that they are persistently aware of the derogatory and demeaning attitudes which they arouse in others. It would then follow that they must *in fact* become self sufficient (e.g., via the symbol of the regular paycheck) before they may ever expect to receive the social approval and acceptance which they need in order to feel whole and human.

Therefore, a presumptively meaningful strategy of treatment in civilian life would be:

(a) that the patient achieve and maintain steady employment within a certain time limit;

(b) that he continue to receive psychiatric support while adjusting himself to the self sufficiency role—such support to continue only until he can manage by himself;

(c) that the treatment facility remain readily available to him when anxiety threatens or when a paternal overseer is indicated.

(2) *Socializing Education*
> Education in the rudiments of successful social
> behavior should be made a part of the treatment
> regime.

One of the more important findings in this study was that the schizophrenic patient possesses such a surprisingly small repertoire of interpersonal behaviors. He is so socially awkward that he many times chooses to present himself as "peculiar" rather than reveal his more terrifying infantilism.

The "tutoring" approach recommended by Sullivan, and previously mentioned (page 43) appears to provide some outline for an eventually useful strategy. Some form of active, member-participation in group functioning appears to be a basic issue and may well hold a key to the eventual eradication of chronicity.

(3) *Specialized Group Therapy*

> Place the patient in a position where he has
> both a regular opportunity to interact with a
> healthy group and the responsibility to do so,

The use of group therapy in this study, *with the attendant staff sitting in as observers,* is an example. Those other investigators who continue to report concerning the interaction between the patient and his family are consistently noting antitherapeutic family situations which appear to prevent the patient from association with the healthy world. If he is allowed to become an operationally anonymous one in his hospital life also, his isolation tendencies will not be countered. There are many strategies which may be used to counter the patient's vicious circle of isolation leading to increased social inadequacy leading to more isolation. The local treatment situation, the facilities available and the imagination of the community would, of course, be primary determinants of the method.

Continuity of vigorous anti-isolation maneuvers, with the responsibility for leadership remaining with the community, would perhaps provide an organizing schema.

ACKNOWLEDGMENTS

This book is dedicated to Bernard Trafficano, Donald Sturges and Charles Johnson, who taught me, more than any others, to appreciate the talents of the Army neuropsychiatric technician.

Success in treatment ventures seemed, to me at least, to depend heavily upon the efforts of such additional staff members as George Combs, Charles Peters, Willie Lyles, Cleveland Jones, James Hulbert, Benjamin Cunningham, Martin Garces, Charles Headon, Kenneth Wolvin, John Marshall, James Merkley, Miles Marcus, Robert Bobst, Preston Carlisle, Huey Strickland, Burton Levy, Thomas White, Robert Purvis, Walter Balcavage, James Godfrey, Joseph Birdsell, Glenn Rucker, Ron Riggs, Donald Couillard, Robert White, Jacob Meinders, Nathan Keston, Dominic Sabatino, Ronald Huntley, Edward Keane, Truman Hanson, Joseph Frankenbeck, Leon Dubay and Jacques Reitz.

May I continue here to acknowledge the project's debt to its many sponsors already listed in *The Symptom as Communication in Schizophrenia*, New York, Grune and Stratton, 1959. Col. William H. Anderson, successor to Lt. Col. Roy E. Clausen as Chief, Department of Neuropsychiatry, Walter Reed General Hospital, continued the tradition of steady support, cooperation and advice.

Psychiatrists contributing by functioning as Ward Officers on the research ward have included Capt. Jason Aronson, MC; Capt. Alexander C. Donald, MC; Capt. Fred G. Hilkert, MC; Maj. Robert F. McKinley, MC; Capt. Richard A. Newman, MC, and Maj. Harold S. Kolmer, MC.

Nurses who have contributed include Maj. Marcia L. Lessard, ANC; Maj. Marguerite Lines, ANC; Capt. Ivie E. Barnes, ANC; Lt. Col. Selma M. Brawner, ANC; Capt. Dolores E. Sheen, ANC and Maj. Jennie L. Caylor, ANC.

Social work officers, whose contributions were crucial to the study, have been mentioned in the text. Their unmentioned assistants were Harry Silverstein and Pearl Mack. The enormous secretarial load has been capably managed by Mrs. Eve Dickman, Mrs. Mary Coffman, Mrs. Marcella Woolston and Miss Norma Wilson. Technical electronic-recording assistance has been provided by Robert F. Conklin and editorial advice by Francis Y. Halsey.

Washington, D.C.   KENNETH L. ARTISS
October 1960   Lieutenant Colonel, MC

REFERENCES AND READING LIST

1. Abrahams, J., and Varon E.: Preliminary report of an experience in the group psychotherapy of schizophrenia. Am. J. Psychiat. *104*: 613-17, 1948.

2. Ackerman, N. W.: Psychoanalysis and group psychotherapy. Group Psychotherapy *3*: 204, 1950.

3. Adams, E. C.: Problems in attitude therapy in a mental hospital. Am. J. Psychiat. *105*: 456-461, 1948.

4. Adland, M. L.: (1) Problems of Administrative Psychotherapy in Mental Hospitals. Psychiat. Quart. Suppl. 1953. (2) Personnel—Effect on patients. Neuropsychiat, 1955.

5. Artiss, K. L., Bushard, B. L., Erikson, K. T., Marlowe, D. H., and Rowe, R. H.: The Symptom as Communication in Schizophrenia. New York, Grune & Stratton, 1959.

6. Artiss, K. L.: Acute Schizophrenic Reaction in a Therapeutic Milieu. Symposium on Preventive and Social Psychiatry, Walter Reed Army Institute of Research, Washington, D.C., April 1957, pp. 517-521. Govt. Prtg. Off., Washington, D.C., 1958.

7. Bachrach, A. J.: Notes on the psychopathology of delusions. Psychiatry *16*: 375-380, 1953.

8. Baker, A. A., Jones, M., Merry, J. and Pomryne, A. B.: A community method of psychotherapy. Brit. J. Med. Psychol. *26*: 222-244, 1953.

9. Bales, R. F.: Interaction Process Analysis. Cambridge, Mass., Addison-Wesley Press, 1950.

10. Barrabee, P. S.: The study of a mental hospital: The effect of its social structure on its functions. Unpub. Ph.D. dissertation, Harvard Univ., Cambridge, 1951.

11. Bateman, L. F., and Dunham, H. W.: The mental hospital in a specialized community experience. Am. J. Psychiat. *105*: 6, 445-448, 1948.

12. Bates, R.: Types of social structure as factors in cures for alcohol addiction. Applied Anthrop. *1*: No. 3, 1-13, 1942.

13. Bellak, L., ed.: Schizophrenia, A Review of the Syndrome. New York Logos Press, 1958.

14. Bettelheim, B.: Love is Not Enough. Glencoe, Ill., Free Press, 1950.

15. Bettelheim, B., and Sylvester, E.: A therapeutic milieu. Am. J. Orthopsychiat. *18*: 191-206, 1948.

16. Bettelheim, B., and Sylvester, E.: The therapeutic influence of the group on the individual. Am. J. Orthopsychiat. *17*: 684-92, 1947.

17. Bion, W. R.: Experiences in Groups. Human Relations, *4*: 2, 314 to *4*: 7, 221, London, Tavistock Pub. Ltd.

18. Boek, W. E., and Boek, J. K.: Society and Health. New York, G. P. Putnam's Sons, 1956.

19. Bond, E.: Dr. Kirkbride and His Mental Hospital. Philadelphia, J. B. Lippincott, 1947.

20. Breckir, N. J.: Group psychotherapy with psychotic patients. Int. J. Group Psychother. *1*: 129, 1951.

21. Brody, E. B., and Redlich, F. C.: Psychotherapy with Schizophrenics. New York, Int'l Univ. Press, Inc., 1951.

22. Brody, M. W.: Observations on "Direct Analysis": The Therapeutic Technique of Dr. John M. Rosen New York, Vantage Press, 1959.

23. Bullard, D. M.: Psychotherapy of paranoid patients. A.M.A. Arch. Gen. Psychiat. *2*: 137-141, 1960.

24. Bullard, D. M.: Problems of clinical administration. Bull. Menninger Clin. *16*: 193-201, 1952.

25. Bullard, O.: The organization of psychoanalytic procedure in the hospital. J. Nerv. & Ment. Dis *91:* 697-703, 1940.

26. Cameron, J. L., Laing, R. D., and McGhie, A.: Patient and nurse: Effects of environmental changes in the care of chronic schizophrenics. Lancet vol. 1384-1386, 1955.

27. Caudill, W.: The Psychiatric Hospital as a Small Society. Cambridge, Mass., Harvard Univ. Press, 1958.

28. Caudill, W., Redlich, F. C., Gilmore, H. R., and Brody, E. B.: Social Structure and Interaction Processes on a Psychiatric Ward. Am. J. Orthopsychiat. *22*: 314-334, 1952.

29. Chapman, R.: Psychoanalysis in a psychiatric hospital. Am. J. Psychiat. *91*: 1093-1101, 1935.

30. Christ, E. A., ed.: Nurses at Work: A Study of Tasks, Attitude Consensus, Work Disparagement and Work Tension in Eight Central Missouri General Hospitals. Columbia, Univ. of Missouri, 1956.

31. Cohen, R. A.: The hospital as a therapeutic instrument. Psychiatry *21*: 29, 1958.

32. Coltharp, R. W.: Group psychotherapy in patients recovering from psychosis. Am. J. Psychiat. *104*: 414, 1947.

33. Cumming, J., and Cumming, E.: Affective symbolism, social norms and mental illness. Psychiatry *19*: 1, 1956.

34. Deardorff, N.: Changing concepts in the care of hospitalized patients. Jewish Social Serv. Quart. *25*: 500, 1949.

35. Dembo, T., and Hanfmann, E.: The patient's psychological situation upon admission to a mental hospital. Am. J. Psychol. *47*: 381-408, 1935.

36. Denber, Herman C. B., ed.: Research Conference Therapeutic Community. Springfield, Ill., Charles C. Thomas, 1960.

37. Deutsch, A.: Shame of the States. New York, Harcourt Brace & Co. Inc., 1948.

38. Deutsch, A.: The Mentally Ill in America. New York, Columbia Univ. Press, 1938.

39. Devereux, G.: The social structure of the hospital as a factor in total therapy. Am. J. Orthopsychiat. *19*: 492-500, 1949.

40. Devereux, G.: The social structure of a schizophrenia ward and its therapeutic fitness. J. Clin. Psychopathol. *6:* 231-265, 1944.

41. Eichert, A. H.: Morale and the Attendant. Ment. Hyg. *28*: 632-638, 1944.

42. Enelow, A. J.: Environmental treatment of psychosis. Psychiatric Quart. *26:* Suppl. 1, 44-52, 1952.

43. Evseef, G. S.: Group psychotherapy in the state hospital. Dis Nerv. System *9*: 214, 1948.

44. Ewald, F. R., Freeman, W., and Watts, J. W.: Psychosurgery: The nursing problem. Am. J. Nursing, *47*: 210-213, 1947.

45. Fidler, J. W., Jr.: The concept of levels in group therapy with psychotics. Int. J. Group Psychother. *1*: 51, 1951.

46. Fidler, J. W., and Standish, C.: Observations noted during course of group treatment of psychoses. Dis Nerv. System *9*: 24, 1948.

47. Fromm-Reichmann, F.: Principles of Intensive Psychotherapy. Chicago, Univ. of Chicago Press, 1950.

48. Geller, J. J.: A program of group psychotherapy in the treatment of chronic mental illness. Psychiatric Quart. *23*: 425, 1949.

49. Geller, J. J.: Current status of group psychotherapy practices in the state hospitals for mental disease. Group Psychother. *3*: 231, 1950.

50. Gifford S., and MacKenzie, J. A.: Review of literature on group treatment of psychoses. Dis. Nerv. System *9*: 19, 1948.

51. Goffman, E.: The nature of deference and demeanour. Am. Anthrop. *58*: 3, 1956.

52. Goffman, E.: Characteristics of Total Institutions. Symposium on Preventive and Social Psychiatry, Walter Reed Army Institute of Research, Washington, D.C., April 1957, pp. 43-84. Govt. Prtg. Off., Washington, D.C., 1958.

53. Goldfarb, W., and Park, P. D.: Dynamic role of group therapy in the total treatment program of psychotic patients. Am. J. Psychotherapy *5*: 514, 1951.

54. Gosline, E.: A report on the application of group psychotherapy at Utica State Hospital. Psychiat. Quart. Suppl. *25*: 65, 1951.

55. Graeber, M. P., et al.: Group Therapy on an Acute Service. Am. J. Psychiat. *110*: 677, 1954.

56. Gralnick, A., and D'Elia, F.: Role of the Patient in the Therapeutic Community: Patient-participation. Southern Divisional Meeting, Am. Psychiatric Assoc., Miami, 1958.

57. Gray, W.: Group psychotherapy in a state hospital. J. Nerv. & Ment. Dis. *108*: 485, 1948.

58. Green, J. A.: Treatment plan combining group and individual psychotherapeutic procedures in a state mental hospital. Psychiatric Quart. *27:* 245, 1953.

59. Greenblatt, M., et al.: From Custodial to Therapeutic Patient Care in Mental Hospitals. New York, Russell Sage Foundation, 1955.

60. Gruenberg, E. M.: Socially Shared Psychopathology. *In* Explorations in Social Psychiatry, New York, Basic Books, 1958.

61. Hamilton, D. M.: The Psychiatric Hospital as a Cultural Pattern. *In.* Glueck, B., ed.: Current Therapies of Personality Disorder. New York, Grune & Stratton, Inc., pp. 18-35, 1946.

62. Henry, J.: The formal structure of a psychiatric hospital. Psychiatry *17*: 2, 1954.

63. Hill, L. B., and Patton, J. D.: When physical therapy (shock) facilitates psychotherapy. Am. J. Psychiat. *113*: 60, 1956.

64. Hyde, R. W., and York, R. H.: A technique for investigating interpersonal relationships in a mental hospital. J. Abnorm. & Social Psychol. *43*: 287-99, 1948.

65. Hyde, R. W., and Solomon, H. C.: Patient government: A new form of group therapy. Dig. Neurol. Psychiat. *18*: 207, 1950.

66. Hyde, R. W., and Solomon, H. C.: Clinical Management of Psychiatric Hospitals. Connecticut State Med. J. *15*: 391-398, 1951.

67. Jackson, D. D., ed.: The Etiology of Schizophrenia. New York, Basic Books, 1960.

68. Jenkins, R. L., and Curran, F. J.: The evolution of and persistence of groups in a psychiatric observation ward. J. Soc. Psychol. *12*: 279-89, 1940.

69. Jones, M., and Mathews, R. A.: The application of the therapeutic community principle in a state mental health program. Brit. J. M. Psychol. *29*: Part I, 57-62, 1956.

70. Jones, M., and Rapoport, R. N.: Administrative and social psychiatry. Lancet 2: 386-388, 1955.

71. Jones, M.: The Therapeutic Community. New York, Basic Books, 1953.

72. Kasanin, J.: Language and Thought in Schizophrenia. Berkeley, Univ. of Calif. Press, 1944.

73. Klapman, J. W.: Clinical practices of group psychotherapy with psychotics. Int. J. Group Psychother. *1*: 22, 1951.

74. Klemes, M. A.: The therapeutic effect of group morale on a psychiatric hospital ward. Bull. Menninger Clin. *15*: 58, 1951.

75. Kline, N. S., and Drayfus, A.: Group psychotherapy in V. A. hospitals. Am. Jr. Psychiat. *104*: 618, 1948.

76. Knight, R. P.: The Plan of Psychoanalytic Therapy in the Mental Hospital. *In* Glueck, B., ed.: Current Therapies of Personality Disorders. New York, Grune & Stratton, 1946, pp. 58-69.

77. Knight, R. P.: Psychoanalysis of hospitalized patients. Bull. Menninger Clin. *1*: 158-167, 1937.

78. Kraus, P. S.: Considerations and problems of ward care for schizophrenic patients: Formulation of a total responsibility program. Psychiatry *17*: 283, 1954.

79. Lichtenberg, J. D.: A study of the changing role of the psychiatrist in the state hospital. Psychiatric Quart. *28*: 428-41, 1954.

80. Lidz, R. W., and Lidz, T.: The family environment of Schizophrenic patients. Am. J. Psychiat. *106*: 332-345, 1949.

81. Luchins, A. S.: Group psychotherapy in a closed ward. Am. J. Orthopsychiat. *17*: 511, 1947.

82. Luchins, A. S.: Restructuring social perceptions: A group psychotherapy technique. J. Consult. Psychol. *14*: 446, 1950.

83. MacDonald, J. M., and Daniels, M. L.: The psychiatric ward as a therapeutic community. J. Nerv. Ment. Dis. *124*: 148, 1956.

84. Main, T. F.: The hospital as a therapeutic institution. Bull. Menninger Clin. *10*: 3, 66-70, 1946.

85. Mann, J.: The organization and technique of group treatment of psychoses. Dis. Nerv. System *9*: 46, 1948.

86. Mann, J., and Semrad, E. V.: The use of group therapy in psychoses. J. Social Casework, *29*: 176, 1948.

87. Masserman, J. H.: The Ur Defenses of Mankind. *In* The Practice of Dynamic Psychiatry. Phila., W. B. Saunders, 1955, pp. 465-485.

88. Menninger, W.: Psychoanalytic principles in psychiatric hospital therapy. South. M. J. *32*: 348-354, 1939.

89. Morse, R., and Noble, D.: Joint endeavors of the administrative physician and psychotherapist. Psychiatric Quart. *16*: 578-585, 1942.

90. Myers, J. M.: The role of the administrative psychiatrist in intensive psychotherapy in a mental hospital. Am. J. Psychiat. *113*: 1, 71-74, 1956.

91. Myerson, A.: Theory and principles of the "total push" method in the treatment of chronic schizophrenia. Am. J. Psychiat. *95*: 1197, 1939.

92. Neuropsychiatric Bibliography for World War II, Sec. I (674 refs.). Psychiatry and Neurology Consultant's Division, U.S. Surgeon General's Office, Washington, D.C., Dec. 1946.

93. Neuropsychiatric Bibliography for World War II, Sec. II (592 refs.). Psychiatry and Neurology Consultant's Division, U.S. Surgeon General's Office, Washington, D.C., Mar. 1947.

94. Powdermaker, F. B., and Frank, J. D., et. al.: Group Psychotherapy Studies in Methodology of Research and Therapy. Washington, D.C., Howard Univ. Press, 1953.

95. Redl, F., and Wineman, D.: Children Who Hate. Glencoe, Ill., Free Press, 1951.

96. Redl, F., and Wineman, D.: Controls From Within. Glencoe, Ill. Free Press, 1951.

97. Rees, T. P., and Glatt, M. M.: The organization of a mental hospital on the basis of group participation. Int. J. Group Psychother. 5: 157-161, 1955.

98. Reider, N.: Hospital care of patients undergoing psychoanalysis. Bull. Menninger Clin. 1: 168-175, 1937.

99. Reisman, D., Glazer, N., and Denny, R.: The Lonely Crowd. New Haven, Yale Univ. Press, 1950.

100. Rodeman, C. R.: The Nursing Service in Milieu Therapy. Walter Reed Army Institute of Research, U.S. Govt. Prtg. Off., Washington, D.C., 1960.

101. Rodeman, C. R.: Guide for Psychiatric Aides. New York, MacMillan Pub. Co., 1956.

102. Roos, C.: Bibliography of Military Psychiatry 1947-52, (545 rfs.). Armed Forces Medical Library, Ref. Div. Feb. 1953, Washington, D.C.

103. Roos, C., and Barry, J.: Bibliography of Military Psychiatry 1952-58, (736 refs.). U.S. Department of Health, Education and Welfare, Public Health Service, Washington, D.C. 1959, U.S. Govt. Prtg. Off., Washington, D.C.

104. Rosen, J. N.: The treatment of schizophrenic psychosis by direct analytic therapy. Psychiatric Quart. 21: 3-37, 117-119, 1947.

105. Rosen, J. N.: Direct Analysis. New York, Grune & Stratton, 1953.

106. Ross, W. D.: Group psychotherapy with psychotic patients and their relatives. Am. J. Psychiat. 105: 383-86, 1948.

107. Rowland, H.: Friendship patterns in the state mental hospital. Psychiatry 1: 3, 367, 1938.

108. Rowland, H.: Interaction processes in the state mental hospital. Psychiatry 1: 323-337, 1938.

109. Ruesch, J., and Bateson, G.: Communication: The social matrix of psychiatry, New York, W. W. Norton Co., 1951.

110. Schwartz, C. G.: Problems for psychiatric nurses in playing a new role on a mental hospital ward. Unpublished manuscript, 1956.

111. Schwartz, C. G.: Rehabilitation of Mental Hospital Patients (Review of the Literature). Public Health Monograph No. 17, 1953.

112. Schwartz, M. S.: Social interaction on a disturbed ward of a mental hospital. Unpublished dissertation, Dept. Sociology, Univ. of Chicago, 1951.

113. Schwartz, M. S.: Social Research in the Mental Hospital. *In* Rose, A. M., ed.; Mental Health and Mental Disorder. New York, W. W. Norton & Co., 1955.

114. Schwartz, M. S., and Shockley, E. L.: The Nurse and the Mental Patient: A Study in Interpersonal Relations. New York, Russell Sage Foundation, 1956.

115. Schwartz, M. S., and Stanton, A. H.: A social psychological study of incontinence. Psychiatry. *13*: 4, 1950.

116. Schwartz, M. S., and Will, G. T.: Low morale and mutual withdrawal on a mental hospital ward. Psychiatry *16*: 4, 1953.

117. Searles, H. F.: The effort to drive the other person crazy—An element in the aetiology and psychotherapy of schizophrenia. Brit. J. M. Psychol. *32*: Part I, 1-18, 1959.

118. Sheimo, S. L., Paynter, J., and Szurek, S. A.: Problems of staff interaction with spontaneous group formations on a children's psychiatric ward. Am. J. Orthopsychiat. *19:* 599-611, 1949.

119. Shellhase, L. J.: Acceptance of role and resultant interaction in the group psychotherapy of schizophrenia. Group Psychotherapy *13:* Nos. 3-4, 208-229, 1961.

120. Shellhase, L. J.: A study of the self-governing activities of a schizophrenic group. Int. J. Soc. Psychiat. (In press.)

121. Shellhase, L. J.: An experience in interdisciplinary research. Unpublished manuscript.

122. Simmel, E.: The psychoanalytic sanitarium and the psychoanalytic movement. Bull. Menninger Clin. *1*: 133-143, 1937.

123. Sivadon, P., and Chanoit, P.: L'ergotherapie on C.T.R.S. de Ville-Evrard Annales Medico-Psychologiques. Paris, 116, vol. 2 (3), 552, Oct. 1958.

124. Slavson, S. R., ed.: Fields of Group Psychotherapy. New York, International Univ. Press, 1956.

125. Slotkin, J. S.: Nature and effects of interaction among schizophrenics. J. Abnorm. & Social Psychol. *37*: 345-368, 1942.

126. Smith, H.: The sociological study of hospitals. Unpub. Ph.D. thesis, Univ. of Chicago, 1949.

127. Sofer, C.: Reactions to administrative change: A study of staff relations in three British hospitals. Hum. Relations 8: 291-316, 1955.

128. Standish, C. T., et al.: Some difficulties in group psychotherapy with psychotics. Amer. J. Psychiat. 109: 283, 1952.

129. Stanton, A. H., and Schwartz, M. S.: Observations on dissociation as social participation. Psychiatry 12: 339-354, 1949.

130. Stanton, A. H.: Psychiatric theory and institutional context. Psychiatry 17: 1, 1954.

131. Stanton, A. H., and Rioch, D. McK.: Milieu therapy. In: Psychiatric treatment. A. Res. Nerv. & Ment. Dis. Proc. 31: 94-105, 1953.

132. Stanton, A. H., and Schwartz, M. S.: The Mental Hospital. New York, Basic Books, 1954, p. 73.

133. Stanton, A. H., and Schwartz, M. S.: Medical opinion and the social context in the mental hospital. Psychiatry 12: 3, 1949.

134. Stanton, A. H., and Schwartz, M. S.: The management of a type of institutional participation in mental illness. Psychiatry 12: 1, 1949.

135. Sullivan, H. S.: The modified psychoanalytic treatment of schizophrenia. Am. J. Psychiat. 10: 519-540, 1931.

136. Sullivan, H. S.: Socio-psychiatric research: Its implications for the schizophrenia problem and for mental hygiene, Am. J. Psychiat. 10: 977-991, 1931.

137. Sullivan, H. S.: Conceptions of modern psychiatry. Psychiatry 3: 1-117, 1940; 8: 177-205, 1945.

138. Sullivan, H. S.: The illusion of personal individuality. Psychiatry 13: 317-332, 1950.

139. Szurek, S. A.: The family and the staff in hospital psychiatric therapy of children. Am. J. Orthopsychiat. 21: 597-611, 1951.

140. Szurek, S. A.: Dynamics of staff interaction in hospital psychiatric treatment of children. Am. J. Orthopsychiat. 17: 652-664, 1947.

141. Taxel, H.: Authority Structure in a Mental Hospital Ward. Unpub. M.S. thesis, Univ. of Chicago, 1953.

142. Thurston, J.: The patients rule themselves. Smith Coll. Studies in Social Work 22: 27-51, 1951.

143. Tudor, G. E.: A sociopsychiatric nursing approach to intervention in a problem of mutual withdrawal on a mental hospital ward. Psychiatry 15: 2, 1952.

144. Walk, A.: Some aspects of the 'moral treatment' of the insane up to 1854. J. Ment. Sc. 100: 421, 807-837, 1954.

145. Weinberg, S. V.: Society and Personality Disorders. In Care and Custody. New York, Prentice-Hall, 1952.

146. Wender, H. B.: Experiences in group psychotherapy with insulin-treated patients. Psychiatric Quart. 24: 312, 1950.

147. Wesson, A. F.: The Social Structure of a Modern Hospital. Ph.D. thesis, Yale University, 1951.

148. Will, O. A.: Human relatedness and the schizophrenic reaction. Psychiatry. 22: 3, 205-223, 1959.

149. Willis, S. E.: The treatment milieu—Its importance in the prognosis of the schizophrenics. U.S. Armed Forces M. J. 5: 704, 1954.

150. Wilmer, H. A.: Social Psychiatry in Action: A Therapeutic Community. Springfield, Ill., Charles C. Thomas, 1958.

151. Willner, G. P.: Preliminary report of the introduction of group psychotherapy on a chronic ward in a mental hospital. Psychiatric Quart. Suppl. 26: 86, 1952.

152. Willner, G. P.: Report on further developments in group psychotherapy on a chronic service of a mental hospital. Psychiatric Quart. 28: 54, 1954.

153. Willoughby, R. H.: The Attendant in the State Mental Hospital. Unpub. M.A. thesis, Univ. of Chicago, 1953.

154. Wolff, K. H.: The Sociology of Georg Simmel. Glencoe, Ill., The Free Press, 1950.

155. Zaniecki, F.: Social groups as products of participating individuals. Am. J. Sociol. 44: 799-811, 1939.

INDEX